PREFACE

'A well-digested history of this irregular order of medical practitioners would not be uninstructive. It would present to us a curious list of priests and nobles, philosophers, simpletons, and knaves. Even Royalty itself would not be absent from it.'

It is nearly one hundred years since Sir Benjamin Collins Brodie wrote these words and it seems incredible that nobody has yet attempted a History of Quackery. In this book I have not tried to comment on the vast army of Continental Quacks, but have limited myself mainly to the English speaking brethren with one or two notable exceptions.

Whenever possible I have quoted from original sources. Spelling has always seemed to me to be a difficult subject. For this reason I have taken the liberty of modernising this wherever it seemed feasible.

ERIC JAMESON

ACKNOWLEDGEMENTS

Writing a book like this involves many people. First of all I would thank the Registrar of the Royal College of Physicians for his permission to quote from the College Annals. Secondly the Staff of the Wellcome Historical Medical Library, who have always been most kind and co-operative. Without their help the task would have been impossible. I am also indebted to the Wellcome Institute for most of the illustrations. The American Medical Association have kindly allowed me to quote from their publications and use some of their illustrations, and I also acknowledge information obtained from the following sources:

The Monthly Review; handbills and newspapers in the British Museum Collections; *The Gentleman's Magazine; The Scots Magazine; The European Magazine; Notes and Queries* (various series); *The Spectator* (*1710–1714*); *The Literary World, 1800; The Annual Register; The Dictionary of National Biography; Monthly Magazine; The Daily Telegraph; Spectator, 28/10/60; The British Medical Journal; Young Ladies Journal, 1892.*

Finally I would like to thank Dr Harvey Flack, who encouraged me to write this book, and Miss Marjorie Vaughan and Mlle Danièle Amblard, whose hard work and advice have been invaluable.

CONTENTS

ILLUSTRATIONS

AN ANECDOTE
OF THE
LATE, CELEBRATED, DR ROCK

'He was standing one day at his door on Ludgate Hill, when a real doctor of Physic passed, who had learning and abilities, but whose modesty was the true cause of his poverty.

' "How comes it," says he to the Quack, "that you without education, without skill, without the least knowledge of science, are enabled to live in the style you do? – You keep your town house, your carriage and your country house: whilst I, allowed to possess some knowledge, have neither, and can hardly pick up a subsistence!"

' "Why, look ye," said Rock smiling, "how many people do you think have passed since you asked me the question?"

' "Why?", answered the Doctor, "Perhaps a hundred."

' "And how many out of those hundred, think you possess common sense?"

' "Possibly one," answered the Doctor.

' "Then," said Rock, "That one comes to you: and I take care of the other ninety nine." '

From the Northern Impostor, *being a faithful narrative of the Life, Adventures and Deceptions of James George Semple, commonly called Major Semple.*

PRINTED FOR G. KEARSLEY, 46, FLEET ST, AND SOLD BY ALL BOOKSELLERS, 1786.

1

INTRODUCTION

This is not a moral book. Many of the characters in it are definitely immoral. Others are almost gentlemen. Neither is the story of Quackery for the excessively squeamish. Quacks, to be successful, desperately need a popular appeal. What appeals to one age may seem crude to another. They also have no time for respectability or convention and some of the most active fields of Quack practice are to be found in subjects sometimes taboo to general society.

Of the many dubious aphorisms that have crept into the English language over recent years, few can be less true than the assertion that 'Cheats never prosper.' Everywhere we look in our 20th-century world we see Cheats not only prospering but enjoying palmy days such as they have never had. Cheating today has grown enormously from its early beginnings in short weight and adulteration. The old days of putting sand in the sugar and a thumb on the scales are over, very nearly that is. The weight of a loaf, the fat content of milk and even the amount of alcohol in a bottle of whisky can be nicely tied up by scientists and Government Inspectors. But man, with his inherent ingenuity has extended Cheating right out of the range of canny scientists or clever legislators. As a result the Spiv was born. The percentage or discount man has evolved, and an 'expense account society' has been created. Financiers' reputations have probably never been so questionable since the South Sea Bubble burst. Cheating has even crept into sport. Horses and dogs are doped with such regularity that it would seem hardly worth while for punters to study the form book. Even Olympic athletes are given 'pep pills' to increase their performance.

13

Gamesmanship, or the art of winning without actually cheating has certainly come to stay.

Although the mechanism of cheating has altered as man became more clever, there are some facets of this interesting phenomenon that have changed little since the Stone Age. One of these is Medical Quackery. The inherent psychology of a Quack's approach to his patient has altered very little since the dim and distant past. All that has changed is his patter.

There seems to be an idea that Quackery was abolished with the introduction of the National Health Service. If we think that we are through with Quacks, all well and good. Unfortunately the Quacks are not through with us! Why should they be? There are still the rich rewards to be had. To see the principles of Quackery gradually crystallising into a regular pattern it is necessary to look back into history. Initially here, we are unfortunately in the 'never, never' land of conjecture and opinion. Our Stone Age ancestors did not leave us much to work upon if we want to decide whether they consulted a priest, doctor or Quack when they were ill. It is just possible that the latter might be the case.

A French cave painting in Ariège, thought to be the creation of a Cromagnon man living some 39,000 years ago is interesting in this respect. It is of a human figure, naked below the waist, with a skin around his shoulders and a pair of deer's antlers on his head. Similar use of weird costume and head-dress is of course seen in primitive societies the world over. It has been customary to refer to such flamboyant characters as Witch Doctors or 'medicine men.' These phrases have been coined in modern times, however, and serious writers on primitive societies and times do not seem to use them. Priests there were in great numbers, leading worship of various deities. Doctors there may have been, either men or women, we do not know, who made serious attempts to tend the ill and the injured. But the Medicine Man type of figure that seems to have survived most successfully in primitive African societies is much more allied to the spirit of Quackery than that of Medicine.

With the advent of the written word our knowledge of Quackery becomes more precise. We know that Quacks lived alongside 'orthodox' practitioners and priests in the earliest Babylonian and Greek societies. In the latter they sold anything

to the credulous from love philtres to cosmetics, and by the time
that the Roman civilisations were evolved they had established
themselves a definite niche in Society from which they have
never been dislodged.

In a showcase in the Roman Life room at the British Museum
is a small rectangular piece of greenish coloured stone. It is
slightly smaller than a packet of cigarettes and about half as
thick. It feels comfortingly smooth to the touch and might pass
for a decorative tile but for one feature. Along its edges some
letters are cut out. These appear unintelligible at first glance
but on closer examination it is obvious that they are mirror
images of words quite easily translatable by anyone possessing
knowledge of schoolboy Latin. They are, in fact, small printing
stamps that will, if pressed into something soft, print words
clearly and effectively. Such a pressing might give us the following sentence. 'Saffron ointment of Junius Taurus, for scars and
discharges, from the recipe of Paccius.'

The specimen we have mentioned was found in archaeological
diggings at Naix in the Meuse area of France. Similar stamps
have been discovered all over Europe in large numbers. One found
in Kenchester, Hereford, mentions 'T. Vindaius Ariovestus,'
and his 'unbeatable' ointment made of a 'preparation of aniseed'
and called 'Chloron the green salve.' Other specimens from
London, Colchester, Cirencester, Norwich, and even Tipperary
show an almost startling similarity. They are nearly all made
in the same green Stearite. They all will print clearly a man's
name and the directions for using a described medicament.

These stamps which were used by wandering Oculist Quacks
in Roman times gave us a tangible link with the past in a way
that makes history live. Not only were men earning their living
by Quackery in Roman times in Europe, but apparently they
existed in great numbers. Their ingenuity devised a method of
labelling their products, simple eye salves, in a way that would
be quick, efficient and economical. Also they were full of good
business ideas. The inclusion of their names and a little 'puff'
about their products put them fair and square outside the conventional medicine of their times into the interesting field of
Quackery.

The eye salves themselves were as numerous and varied as
their manufacturers. Some had to be dissolved in water and put

into the eye on a probe such as one made by Lucius Vallantinus for 'Cicatrices and Granulations.' Others had to be mixed with milk or other fluids. One for 'sore eyes caused by a strong light' had to be mixed with the white of an egg. Many of the names of the Quacks' remedies stem from the Greek. For instance, a salve using bile as its chief medical constituent would be called Diacholes, or one using plant juices Diachylum. Thus, in all probability, the clever Roman Quacks were merely using remedies well known to their Greek antecedents. The writings of ancient regular physicians often mention hordes of Quacks who by 'making a great display in the train of a learned Doctor no sooner hear of a patient than they hurry off to fill his ears with their own medical ability.'

The *Arabian Nights*, although a comparatively modern work contains many traditional tales that are probably very old and come from stories told well before the Birth of Christ. Such a tale tells of the Great Physician Galen, meeting a Quack. Galen, practising in the A.D. 160's was a pretty strict doctor who we would now describe as 'of the old school.' He advocated 'self-control of a high order and the ignoring of life of pleasure.' He also advised 'quiet behaviour in the sick-room by the physician,' and deplored 'untimely or too frequent visits' by doctors.

He would not have been very pleased, therefore, when a Quack set up his stall in the courtyard of his house. The gentleman in question was not a Quack by choice but rather had the mantle thrust upon him by his wife, who found that her weaver husband was not supporting her as she was accustomed. She was a noble woman who had married beneath her, on the proviso that her husband was always 'under her order to bid and forbid and would never thwart her in word or deed.' The unfortunate man bound himself in writing to pay 'ten thousand Dirham in default.'

One day this surprisingly shrewish matriarch noticed on her travels how well the travelling Quacks were doing, and hit upon the bright idea that her husband should graduate into this subtle craft. The poor weaver, although having no choice in the matter, learnt his new trade well and was soon travelling far and wide and perhaps even 'sending a little something home each week.' Galen must have heard of the Weaver Quack's skill for he took the trouble to listen to his patter and observe the way in which he impressed patients. He watched a woman in the audience anxiously asking the Quack some questions. After a little while, the following dialogue occurred:

QUACK: Is not your husband a Jew and his ailment Flatulence?

WOMAN (amazed): Yes, what is the remedy for his illness?

QUACK: First bring the honorarium!

This is in the best spirit of Quackery. Galen, who had heard the conference with some interest, noticed that the medicine prescribed by the Weaver was 'such as would only aggravate the complaint,' and so he 'had the offender brought before him.' Eventually he was told the whole sad story of the Weaver's matrimonial troubles. Galen could not resist asking the Quack how 'he knew that the woman was from a man and that he was a stranger and a Jew and that his ailment was flatulence?'

The Quack replied, ' 'Tis well, thou must know that we people of Persia are well skilled in physiognomy, and I saw the woman to be rosy cheeked, blue eyed and tall statured. These qualities belong not to the women of Rome: moreover I saw her burning with anxiety, so I knew that the patient was her husband. As for her strangerhood, I noted that the dress of the woman differed from that of the townsfolk, wherefore I knew she was a foreigner, and in her hand I saw a yellow rag, which told me that the sick man was a Jew and she was a Jewess. Moreover she came to me on the fast day; and 'tis the Jews' custom to take meat puddings and food that have passed the night and eat them on the Saturday, their Sabbath, hot and cold, and they exceed in eating, wherefore flatulence and indigestion betide them. Thus I was directed and guessed that which thou hast heard.'

Galen was so impressed that he directed the Weaver should be given the necessary sum to release him from his scheming wife's clutches, on the proviso that he 'never again took a wife of a higher rank than his own and returned to his proper craft.' In the 'lived happily ever after' tradition we can believe that he did this. But such behaviour would be quite out of character for any self-respecting peripatetic Quack. Much more likely, he would gladly pocket his unexpected windfall and quickly move off to a new pitch in a different city.

A definition of Quackery is really necessary before going any further into the interesting study of Quack psychology. The word 'Quack' is held to have several derivations and many nations seem anxious to claim the dubious privilege of its origin. The Dutch suggest Kwabzalver, from Kwab, a sebaceous cyst, and Zalver an ointment. Doubtless many Quacks offered to cure cysts, or Wens with their favourite ointments. But it is doubtful if the Dutch claim can be held any more than the German one, that the word came from Quecksilver, the Teutonic version of quicksilver – a substance much used in 18th-century Medicine and Quackery. An interesting if rather far-fetched idea is that Quack was a derivative of Quake. The intermittent fevers prevalent in marshy districts, that we now presume to have been malarial in origin, were in some localities known as the Quakes and the doctors who treated them were called Quake Doctors.

The most feasible definition gives both an etymological and practical explanation of the word. *Skeats Dictionary* gives the meaning of 'to quack,' as to 'cry out pretended nostrums,' and draws attention to the fact that it is only a specialised use of the plain English meaning, 'to make a noise like a duck.' This brings us to the essence of Quackery. Quacks must make a noise to get themselves noticed. The particular type of noise they make has altered from time to time, but it is the principle of self-advertisement that really defines Quackery.

If it is to flourish effectively there must be a credulous public. Credulity has been described as 'a monarch on whose kingdom the sun never sets. The cradle and the grave are its frontiers, the entire human race are its subjects.' It might be argued that with increased standards of education the kingdom would shrink. This could have happened if Quacks had not moved with the times. A 17th-century Quack would not hold his own today. But incredibly enough as the public has changed with regard to its general level of education, Quacks have found it just as easy to appeal to man's credulity.

Quackery has sometimes been associated with the lack of medical qualification, although Quacks existed long before doctors took examinations. Recently a new term has crept into the English language – Fringe Medicine. It is applied to a whole host of irregular practitioners, some qualified in medicine, for example the Homeopaths, and others unqualified, such as the Naturopaths. Many Fringe Practitioners are out and out Quacks and others, conversely, are most professional in their demeanour. To get English Quackery into perspective it is probably best to consider it first of all in the days when Fringe Medicine would have been hard to define, as medical qualifications did not exist.

With the fall of the Greco-Roman civilisations around the year A.D. 200, a period of 1,000 years of darkness began as far as medicine was concerned, which lasted until about A.D. 1200. Anything scientific was forgotten. Whoever practised the healing art at this time probably did so equally as well or badly as his rival, so the period holds little interest for us as far as the Natural History of Quackery is concerned.

The philosophy of a practising physician who lived at Salerno round about the year 1100 will serve as an example of orthodox medicine at this time. He advised that 'When called to a patient commend yourself to God and to the angel who guided Tobias. On the way, learn as much as possible from the messenger, so that if you discover nothing from the patient's pulse or water, you may still astonish him and gain his confidence by your knowledge of the case. On arrival ask the friends whether the patient has confessed, for if you bid him do so after the examination it will frighten him. Then sit down, take a drink and praise the beauty of the country and the house, if they deserve it, or extrol the liberality of the family.

Next proceed to feel his pulse, remembering it may be affected by your arrival, or, the patient being a miser, by his thinking of the fee. Do not be in a hurry to give an opinion, for the friends will be more grateful for your judgement if they have to wait for it. Tell the patient you will cure him, with God's help, but inform the friends that the case is a most serious one. Look not desirously on the man's wife, daughter, or handmaid, for this blinds the eyes of the physician, deprives him of the divine assistance, and disturbs the patient's mind.

'If, according to custom, you are asked to dinner, do not hasten to take the first place, unless, as is usual for the priest and the physician, it is offered to you. Often send to enquire how the patient is, that he may see you do not neglect him for the pleasures of the table, and on leaving express your thanks for the attention shown to you, for this will please him much.'

The gradual evolution of medicine from its confused state in Norman times up until the beginning of the 17th century is not the province of this book. Interested readers are referred to the many excellent works on this subject. Our concern, at the moment, is in Quackery and its relationship to orthodox medicine.

Tudor times were wonderful days for Quacks. An anonymous publication, *The Anatomies of the True Physician and Counterfeit Mountebank* (1605), gives us a good word picture of the veritable army of Quacks that regularly marched through England at this time. They were: 'Runagate Jews, the cut-throats and robbers of Christians, slow-bellied monks who had made escape from their cloisters, Simoniacal and perjured shavelings, busy St John-lack-Latins, thrasonical and unlettered chemists, shifting and outcast pettifoggers, light-headed and trivial druggers and apothecaries, sun-shunning night-birds and corner creepers, dull-pated and base mechanics, stage players, jugglers, pedlars, prittle-prattling barbers, filthy graziers, curious bath-keepers, common shifters and cogging cavaliers, bragging soldiers, lazy clowns, one-eyed and lamed fencers, toothless and tattling old wives, chattering charwomen and nurse-keepers, 'scape-Tyburns, dog-leeches and suchlike baggage. In the next rank, to second this goodly troupe, follow poisoners, enchanters, wizards, fortune tellers, magicians, witches and hags.'

The Quack legions were clearly on the march and going into battle regularly. But a rival army was being mustered. Slowly the forces of professionalism were making themselves felt. These were the Barber Surgeons, Apothecaries and Physicians. Unfortunately these forces were not united in their attacks on the strongholds of Quackery, and they often fell into irregular battles between themselves. Frequent sniping activities went on, even within their individual ranks.

The Barber Surgeons amalgamated in 1504 to form a company so that only their members could, 'within the City of London, suburbs and a mile compass of the City,' practise any 'barbary or shavery, surgery, letting of blood, or any other thing belonging to surgery, drawing of teeth only excepted.' This uneasy alliance of two practical arts had many a private battle to fight before Surgery became established as a very respectable profession in 1800, when the College of Surgeons was formed.

Many thoroughly bad surgeons, probably no better than Quacks, existed. John Halle, a member of the Worshipful Company of Surgeons himself and a practising Surgeon in Maidstone,

Kent, wrote, in 1565, 'an Exposition against abuses of Surgery and Physic.'

As a result he became graced with the title of 'The Quacks' Harrier.' He lamented that, 'whereas there is one Surgeon that was apprenticed to his Art, and one Physician that has travelled in the true study and exercise of Physic, there are ten that are presumptuous smearers, smatterers and abusers of the same; yea, smiths, cutlers, carters, cobblers, coopers, carriers of leather, carpenters, and a great rabble of women.' He also accused ignorant surgeons of running about the country like 'pedlars, tinkers, rat-catchers and very vagabonds,' and said there was less attention paid to the making of good Surgeons than to other artificers. 'Alas, there are goodly orders taken, and profitable laws made, for making cloth, tanning of leather, making shoes and other external things, but not for making Surgeons.'

The blame for the poor quality of Surgery he attributed to bad teaching of Apprentices by their Masters. Apparently the Surgeons made their charges 'do the toil in their house and not make them cunning men.' As a result of this many Apprentices, after their seven years' 'training,' could only 'poule or shave, draw a tooth or dress a broken pate.' He urged his colleagues not to 'steal like robbers, the service of your Apprentices, when, contrary to your covenants, you hide your science from your servants.'

Warming to his subject, Quack Surgeons, he asked, 'Why is every rude rustic, brainsick beast, fond fool, indiscrete idiot, yea bedlem bourde and scalding drab suffered thus.' John Halle also made known his ideas on the qualities that a Surgeon should have. 'A Surgeon should not be mis-created, deformed, goggle or squint eye, unhealthy of body, imperfect of mind, not whole in his members, nor boisterous of fingers, or have shaking hands.' On the more positive side he suggests that a Surgeon should 'have the heart of a lion, eyes like a hawk, and the hands of a woman.' He also advised his colleagues to be 'well-mannered, gentle, sober, meek, merciful – no extortioner, and so accomplish his hand at the rich that he may help the poor for the sake of God.'

These were high ideals in the 16th century and it is no wonder that Halle found among his colleagues, 'so many sheep heads, unwitty, unlearned, unchaste, ribald, lechers, fornicators, drunkards, bellygods, and envious, evil mannered men,' who, 'thus miserably be suffered to abuse so noble an art.'

An example of the haphazard methods of surgical training in the 17th century is given by Daniel Turner. A barber's apprentice would elect to go to sea and 'without difficulty after his first or 2nd voyage, become a Surgeon's mate.' After a few such trips a Surgeon's mate would establish himself as a fully fledged Surgeon and discourse freely on 'fractures, dislocations, gangrenes, malformations and amputations.' Such gentlemen were commonly known as 'Sea professors.' It is not surprising that Halle advised a more effective surgical training and told his students to 'let their book be their pastime and game, yea, thou must desire it as the child doth his mother's pap, so will it nourish thee.'

• If the Surgeons were pulling their socks up a bit and attempting even in a half-hearted manner to improve standards of practice, and so limit Quackery, the Physicians were doing likewise. King Henry VIII's original medical statute in 1511 contained the following words, 'the science and cunning of physic and surgery were daily . . . exercised by a great multitude of ignorant persons of whom the greater part had no manner of insight in the same, nor any other kind of learning: some also con no letters on the book, so far forth that common artificers as Smiths and Weavers and Women, accustomably take upon them great cures and things of great difficulty in which they partly use sorcery and witchcraft, partly apply such medicine unto the diseases as can be very noxious, to the great injury of the faculty and the grievous hurt and destruction of many of the King's liege people, most especially them that cannot discern the uncunning from the cunning.'

The Statute went on to state that none should practise as a physician or surgeon (within seven miles of the city), except he first be approved and admitted by the Bishop of London or Dean of St Paul's. These ecclesiastics had to call together 'four doctors of physic, and for surgery other expert persons in that faculty.' Outside the city limits Bishops were empowered with similar authority.

Judging by results the Statute did not have much practical effect in controlling bad surgery. The Physicians acted on it rather more vigorously, for in 1518 the great Thomas Linacre persuaded the King to give a charter to the College of Physicians. Thus the Royal College of Physicians was founded and new life given to the oldest Medical Institution in Europe. The power of licensing Physicians, within the seven-mile limit, was thus transferred from the clerics to the doctors.

It must not be thought that no qualified physicians existed prior to this date. The reverse is true. Oxford and Cambridge and many Continental universities had been granting M.D.s for many years. At English universities standards were very variable and largely academic. Apart from Leyden and Montpellier the Continental ones were probably worse. Our universities produced 'Latined scholars,' who could not, unless they went to the Continent to finish their training, have had much clinical experience. Conventional medicine still subscribed to the Galenic Humoral theory. Much of their thinking was muddled and obscure, and this of course gave added power to the elbow, or rather the lungs of their sworn enemies, the Quacks.

But the newly constituted Royal College of Physicians busied themselves with many things. Perhaps the most important was that they eventually started to hold regular examinations at the College. A peep over the shoulder of the President holding what amounts to a 17th-century Final Examination gives us an interesting opportunity of seeing a Quack squirming before his persecutors and yet still trying desperately to talk himself out of trouble.

One unfortunate candidate was Dr Eyre. As Eyre trudged through the muddy London streets on a dark and damp November afternoon on his way to the Royal College of Physicians, he must have been dreading the ordeal before him. He had had trouble with the College before, having been hauled over the coals and heavily fined for practising within the College's jurisdiction without a licence. Once previously he had tried, unsuccessfully, to bluff a licence from the President by pleading that he was 'peaceable, and begged for grace because he was born here, and lived here even though he practised medicine in out-of-the-way places and in neighbouring districts.' The President was not impressed by this and curtly told him that he must take his examination.

Now, on the 4th November, 1614, he was up before the Censors once more to try for the coveted licence. The College had only recently moved from its old premises in Linacre's house at Knight Rider Street, to Amen Corner, at the end of Paternoster Row. As Eyre turned into the Row, he would have seen the handsome twenty-one-roomed house at the end of the street, separated from the Stationer's Hall by a narrow courtyard. The herb garden, now damp and dejected, would have been still full of flowers when he made his previous appearance at the College, and its melancholy winter aspect must have been a depressing sight.

Entering the College through a large central doorway Eyre would find himself in a spacious hall, on his left was an elegant parlour from which opened a door leading into the herb garden. After having been asked to wait for a few minutes in the hall Eyre would have been eventually conducted through a small study on the right-hand side of the hall, into the great chamber where the President and his Censors were arrayed in all their glory. The examination was about to commence.

In the old College Annals we read that Dr Eyre, 'making use of a language very much like Latin promised to do his best.' The President and half a dozen or so Censors glaring across the table at him, had probably unnerved him for, on being asked 'what was the number of natural things forming part of ourselves?' he replied that 'he had read about these today but now indeed they were forgotten!' He added, rather irrelevantly, that he was 'engaged in subjects relating to women.' The Annals of the Royal College of Physicians comment in what is the nearest thing to a joke in these august documents, 'although he was a bachelor.' (If the censor's questions seem a little strange to 20th-century ears, it must be remembered that he was merely seeking Dr Eyre's knowledge of the 'elements, temperaments, humours, spirits, etc.;' that were part and parcel of the first principles of 17th-century medical knowledge.)

The Censor continued the viva by asking, 'What is an element?' Dr Eyre replied that 'it had no substance.' This was obviously the wrong thing to say for the Censor immediately launched himself into a long diatribe on elements that must have made the unfortunate candidate shake in his boots. The second Censor took up the cudgels next and asked Eyre, 'how a disease and a fever differed?' Eyre must have felt that he was scoring a point or two, when he replied, 'that a fever is a disease.'

Unfortunately, in 17th-century eyes he was wrong again for as the Censor rather obtusely put it, 'if he treated a disease that was not a disease then he must treat a fever as it were a disease!' At this the Annals tell us 'the candidate muttered.'

Continuing, the Censor asked Dr Eyre the 'number of the temperaments.' The poor Quack was failing badly now, as he merely said 'that he had read THAT today, but now did not remember.' After this gaff the Registrar, who had kept silent up until now stated that, 'he marvelled that he had done so much and was esteemed so highly among others.' The examination dragged on, the Quack not making much impression on his examiners until at last the Censor said in exasperation 'he had nothing more to ask from a man that could not answer.' This was the end as far as Eyre was concerned. He had obviously failed. The President in a kindly vein, 'encouraged him not to give up hope as no other charge had been made against him.' Strange to say Eyre eventually gained his licence at a later date. The Censors were then still not over-enthusiastic about his ability as they earnestly advised him to call in one of his colleagues if he was ever at a loss to know what to do for the best.

Another candidate for licence was Mr Theodore Naileman. He had sent the President a letter of recommendation from the Duchess of Richmond. It was not at all uncommon for prospective candidates to send letters of recommendation to the College before they took their examinations. One notorious Quack actually produced a recommendation from the Queen herself. These testimonials did not seem to impress the President or his Censors unduly.

The first Censor to examine Naileman was, appropriately enough, Dr Fox. The following dialogue took place:

DR FOX: Where were you first initiated in these mysteries of medicine?
NAILEMAN: I forget a little because of a fractured cranium.
DR FOX: What injured part affected the memory?
NAILEMAN: I refer to the occiput.
DR FOX: Why did you rather lose your Latin than English?

(Dr Fox should perhaps have known that in traumatic amnesia, the most recently learnt faculties are the most easily damaged. But he did not and neither apparently did Naileman, as his answer shows.)

NAILEMAN: By want of using it.
DR FOX: What part were you hurt in?
NAILEMAN: The middlemost. The head is divided into three parts.
DR FOX: Which are they?
NAILEMAN: The sutures.
DR FOX: What is the suture (that) runs down the head?
NAILEMAN: The Coronal.

Having got something right the candidate might well have breathed a sigh of relief. But he was to receive no quarter. The President took over.

PRESIDENT: What books have you read of Hippocrates?
NAILEMAN: The Aphorisms in English and Dutch.

This apparently seemed reasonably satisfactory and the next Censor continued the examination.

Sir WILLIAM PADDYE: There be three faculties?
NAILEMAN: Imagination, reason, memory.

Again the candidate seemed to score. The next Censor was Dr Wilson. Perhaps he had some sort of personal interest in Naileman's activities as his first question was:

DR WILSON: What disease did you cure in the Duchess' family?
NAILEMAN: The Yellow Jaundice.
DR WILSON: What is the Yellow Jaundice?
NAILEMAN: The overflowing of the Gaule.
DR WILSON: What part goes it to?
NAILEMAN: To the Mawe.
DR WILSON: What is the Mawe?
NAILEMAN: The place of the first decoction.

A Dr Argent now butts in.

DR ARGENT: When it is (in) the Mawe, which way goes it to the body?
NAILEMAN: By the Vena Cava.

This all seemed satisfactory for a Dr Gifford now asks:

DR GIFFORD: How by the urine will you judge the Jaundice?
NAILEMAN: By the colouring of the cloth.

The President now saw fit to interfere again.

PRESIDENT: Do all Jaundices come by the stopping of Gaule?

Here Naileman cannot answer. This is the first real mistake
he has made, but his lack of Latin has weighed heavily against
him. Also the examiners obviously have not swallowed the
amnesia excuse for not 'remembering' where he learnt the
mysteries of medicine.

PRESIDENT: What other signs are there besides the urine in
Jaundice?
NAILEMAN: Yellowness of the skin, and eyes, by the faintness, and
by the Ordure.

The last Censor concludes.

DR MEVERALL: How many elements (are there)?
NAILEMAN: Four: Air, fire, water, earth.
DR MEVERALL: What is an element?
NAILEMAN: A beginning. An element is that by which its equal
proportions keeps man's body in health.
DR MEVERALL: Are the elements equal in the body?
NAILEMAN: Yes, equally in weight. (This was a mistake. In
Galenic medicine the treatment of disease was based upon the pre-
ponderance and interaction of elements and their qualities; they must
have varied and therefore could not be equal.)

After this the candidate was dismissed and the Censors conferred. Their verdict was – 'He is unsufficient, but for to give
my Lady content, let him be examined again on the first Friday
of next month.'

Naileman, who had spent three years at St John's at Oxford,
and also some time at Leyden, would seem to have been a fairly
good amateur doctor, considering the age in which he lived. He
was obviously not versed in the classics and one gathers that his
successful London Quack practice was an embarrassment to
several of the fashionable Physicians of the day. There is no
evidence that he ever bothered to sit for his licence again.
Probably by moving his sphere of operations a little he was able
to keep out of the notice of the Royal College of Physicians.

The Royal College did not only confine its activities to purely
medical matters. On December 7th, 1627, Dr Price from
Bologna, with ten years' experience there, applied for a licence
to practise in London. In a preliminary interview the President
asked him if he were a Roman Catholic. Dr Price replied in the
affirmative and the President asked him if he would consider

renouncing his religion and 'take the oath toward the King.' Dr Price asked for time to consider the question and apparently thought better of it for he never applied again.

Not all candidates for licences were unlucky. One who proved successful was Dr James Yonge, Fellow of the Royal Society. He had a bishop's licence, but admitted that a licence from the College of Physicians would be a 'feather in his cap.' The President examined him on the processes of nutrition and digestion. A Dr Charlton examined on the subject of the circulation of the blood, gangrene and sciatica. Then Dr Collins, 'a grim, sour old man,' one of whose patients Yonge had seen previously, nearly tripped him up on 'the cause of the heart's motion,' and later on Pleurisy and Paracentesis.

Once the examination was over and the candidate had passed, things became quite jolly. 'When I received their licence, they all complimented me and made me sit down amongst them, at which time my good friend, Dr Gooddall, came in,' Dr Yonge reminisced. 'We sat drinking good ale and claret (at five o'clock in the afternoon), talking sometimes of news and sometimes of Art. I talked with all the boldness and freedom I could on purpose, to let them see all I could to my advantage.'

A licence was not to be had for nothing. £8 went to the College, £1 to the President, 13/4 to the Treasurer, 10/– for writing the certificate, and 6/8 for the beadle. This totals the nice round professional sum of £10 10s. 0d., quite a lot of money in the 17th century.

Quack harrying by means of examinations was not the only activity of the Royal College of Physicians. They also prosecuted Quacks whenever they got a chance. For example Leonard Kerton was 'charged by Mrs Ady and her servant, Helena Layfall, with having given the aforesaid Helena, Mercury pills, due to which she felt worse by salivation'; moreover, he falsely claimed 'that the maid was infected with French Pox (Syphilis).' In his defence, Kerton asserted that he was 'a Surgeon from Bristol.' He stated that he had given Helena a pill made from 'a precipitate of cinnibar and beaver's stones,' for 'an ulcer on her arm and a toph on her forehead.' After hearing the evidence the Censors found him guilty and fined him 40/– or imprisonment. Obviously this, to Kerton, was chicken feed as he 'paid willingly and was dismissed.'

One Doctor licensed by the College in 1684 must have given the Censors and President many an uncomfortable hour for he committed the unpardonable sin of turning Quack after qualification. His name was John Pechey and he had received his M.A. at Oxford (New Inn Hall) in 1678. After graduation he returned to Chichester, where his father was a practising physician and served as his apprentice for six years before he applied to the Royal College for admission as a licentiate. By now the examination was in three parts. The first was in Anatomy and Physiology, the second in Pathology and the third in the use and exercise of Medicine. It is interesting that today Medical students still take their 1st, 2nd and Final M.B. examinations.

Although Pechey failed on his first attempt he eventually qualified and went to practise at Dungate. Apparently this was not a success for during the next three years he spent much of his time writing on medical subjects, one of which was the first translation of Thomas Sydenham's works into English. This could not have been a particularly lucrative occupation and in 1687 Pechey hit on the bright idea of opening up a Public Dispensary. He took, with two colleagues, the lease on the 'Golden Angel and Crown' and started advertising himself in an extravagant way. The following is a description of what patients could expect of the Pechey brand of Physic.

1. A certain time shall be agreed upon for the cure of the diseases before they are undertaken.
2. The sick shall know first what the medicines shall cost that are necessary for their cure: though they shall pay for them only as they use them.
3. Whatever is received for medicines . . . shall be faithfully returned if the case be not perfected within the time prefixed.
4. That they may be sure of having their health or money restored. They or their friends for them, shall have a note if they desire it under my hand or seal for the performance of these proposals.

He then went on to give his charges for visiting the sick which was 2/6 for day visits in the city. If he went out into the suburbs he expected a payment of 2/6 per mile travel allowance as an extra. All fees were payable in advance.

This was all seditious stuff as far as the Profession was concerned. Not only did it infringe the 'no advertising' rule, indigent to medicine, but Pechey's practice of 'no cure, no fee,' and a time limit on cures at that, was more than the College of Physicians could endure. Added to this it must be remembered that most Physicians had direct contact with patients only at the invitation of an Apothecary at this time. The very rich or influential had the privilege of calling in the Physician directly at 2 gns. a visit. But as for sick visiting at 2/6 time, this was clearly cut price medicine that could not be tolerated even in the 17th century.

The Censors soon called Pechey before them and he was promptly admonished for his practices. Admonishing a man like Pechey had roughly the same sort of effect as the pruning of a rose bush. First of all it looks as though you have done a lot of damage, but within a few months it is shooting up again stronger than ever. The next pamphlet that he published came quickly to the point. 'At the Angel & Crown,' it stated, 'there lives John Pechey of long standing in the College of Physicians in London, and because it is commonly reported that physicians will do nothing without their fees, he proposes to undertake certain diseases including deafness, sore eyes, coughs, consumptions, stomach pains, jaundice, fevers and agues, for nothing, till the cure is performed.' Soon after this he advertised that, 'the sick have advice for nothing and the excellent purging pills prepared by John Pechey of the College of Physicians. My elixir for the stone and the cholic cost 2/6.' These two advertisements swamped Pechey with patients, for he was soon doing a roaring trade and was having to charge 6d. for a consultation, presumably as a deterrent.

This sort of practice put Pechey more and more at loggerheads with the Royal College of Physicians, especially as he was now refusing to pay his yearly £2 fee required by statute. When the Beadle called on him to collect this, Pechey told him that he could, 'do what he liked about it as he had no intention of paying.' The College ordered him to be arrested and prosecuted. Understandably, Pechey did not relish a period in one of London's prisons, and moved out of the area of the College's jurisdiction. Nothing more was heard of him, and it may be that he left fringe medicine for regular practice.

Before leaving the early days of English medicine to consider some of the more flamboyant aspects in the Natural History of Quackery, it is worth while mentioning, perhaps to exclude from censure, someone who is often placed in the same dubious category as the Quack. This is the Empiric. There has been a lot of confusion between these 'professions,' but there is no real similarity between them.

An Empiric uses remedies in an experimental way to try to cure disease. Sometimes it will have been noticed that this drug or that herb improved the general condition of a patient suffering from some illness. The true Empiric noted this observation for further use. Such practical knowledge often caused drugs to be eventually included in the therapeutic armamentarium of regular Physicians. The use of digitalis in heart disease and quinine in fevers probably originated in this way.

The true Empiric differentiates himself from the Quack because he never advertises himself or his wares. He also dissociates himself from orthodox medicine, and its sometimes rather hidebound theory and practice. Some Empirics were the traditional 'Ladies of the Manor' who did what they could for the sick by means of a collection of recipes stuck into the back of the family Bible. In all cases they were amateur healers and often their methods had advantages over regular medicine due to their innocuous nature and harmlessness.

One famous Empiric was George Berkeley. This brilliant young man had made his mark in the world of philosophy by the year 1710 when he was only twenty five. He would not have been flattered by our classification of him, as he abhorred 'blind empiric rashness.' He would doubtless have rather been remembered for his philosophical work than as the 'inventor' of 'Tar Water.' In the early days of the 18th century, Berkeley moved in the elegant society of Queen Anne and was friendly with such men as Swift and Samuel Johnson. He became Bishop of Cloyne in 1734. In the course of his ecclesiastical duties he often came in close contact with the sick. In 1744 he published his book, '*Siris, a Chain of Philosophical Reflections and Enquiries on the Virtues of Tar Water*. (Siris, Berkeley's title, is probably an allusion to the ancient Egyptian word for the Nile. Another Siris, the Dog Star, was thought to begin to rise when the Nile was about to flood. The dark healing waters of the Nile were probably in Berkeley's mind when he was philosophing about Tar Water.)

Berkeley first saw Tar Water used when he was living in

America. 'In certain parts of America, Tar Water is made by putting a quart of cold water to a quart of Tar and stirring them together in the vessel, which is then left standing until the tar sinks to the bottom. A glass of clear water being poured off for a draft is then replaced by the same quantity of fresh water, the vessel being left to stand as before.' The economy of such medicine must have appealed to everyone. Had there been a Health Service in the 18th century, Tar Water would have probably been a firm favourite with the Ministry of Health for this very reason.

Berkeley did not agree with this economic method of preparation, as it produced he thought, 'Tar Water of different degrees of strength.' His recipe was one quart of tar to one gallon of water, the mixture being stirred and left to stand for 48 hours. Berkeley mentions that the tar left over, when the 'water' had been decanted off, should be used only for 'common purposes.' Berkeley first tried tar water on cases of Small Pox. He had seen it used with good results on such cases in America. He tried it 'in my own neighbourhood when the Small Pox raged with great virulence. The trial fully answered my expectation, all those within my knowledge who took the Tar Water, either escaped the distemper or had it very favourably.'

He also believed Tar Water efficacious in the treatment of 'Scurvy, Hysteria, Hypochondriacal disorders, Plague, Erysipelas, all disorders of urinary passages, Gout, Gangrene, and the Bloody Flux.' Berkeley's Empiricism is well demonstrated in his recommendation that Tar Water be used in a prophylactic way. This is probably one of the earliest examples of occupational medicine in existence. He gives three examples for Sailors, Students, and Ladies! 'To sailors and all seafaring persons who are subject to scorbutic disorders and putrid fevers, especially on long southern voyages, I am persuaded that Tar Water would be very beneficial.' Similarly he states that 'studious persons, also pent up in narrow holes, breathing bad air and stooping over their books, are much to be pitied. As they are debarred the free use of air and exercise, this (tar water), I will venture to recommend as the best succedaneum to both.' The philosopher was not much impressed with the womenfolk of his day and age as he said that 'this same Tar Water will also give charitable relief to the ladies, who want it more than the parish poor; being many of them never able to make a good meal and sitting pale, puny and forbidden like ghosts at their own table, victims of vapours and indigestion.'

Although Berkeley believed that Tar Water was the 'greatest of all temporal blessings,' and was 'convinced that under providence he owed his life to it,' there is evidence that even then there were agnostics about trying to discredit the Cure. Writing to a friend he said that 'nothing is more difficult and disagreeable than to argue men out of their prejudices: I shall not therefore enter into controversies on this subject, but if men dispute and object, shall leave the decision to time and trial.'

Nowadays, when a new drug treatment is being evaluated, a 'blind trial' is usually carried out. A number of patients suffering from a disease are divided into two groups. Half of these receive tablets of the drug under investigation, and the other half receive indistinguishable dummy tablets. Neither the patients nor the doctors actually working the investigation know exactly which group is getting the new drug. Later, clinical results are collected and conclusions are drawn. Berkeley, showing an intelligence far in advance of his generation, suggested that such an experiment should be carried out with Tar Water. He advised that 'patients should be put into two hospitals at the same time of year and provided with the same necessities of diet and lodging and for further care let one have a tub of Tar Water and an old woman: the other hospital what attendance and drugs you please.'

Had such an experiment been made it would have been obvious exactly what Tar Water would do. Unfortunately it was too advanced a conception for the Age and was never put into practice. Tar Water after enjoying an enormous vogue for some years, gradually went out of favour.

Another Empiric of a rather different type was John Wesley, founder of Methodism. His Empiricism is well displayed in his book, *Primitive Physic*, which first appeared in 1747 when he was forty-four. It was an immediate success and had gone through twenty-three editions by 1791 when Wesley died. Numerous posthumous editions were published in most languages, and there is no doubt that *Primitive Physic* had a great influence on English and American public opinion. The book was sold at all 'Methodist Preaching Houses in town and country,' price 1/–.

B

The full title of the book was *Primitive Physic or an Easy and Natural Method of Curing most Diseases*. It was Wesley's theory that, due to man's original sin, various diseases were foisted on him by the Devil, but a beneficent Maker had provided in the universe cures for all these diseases. The only trouble was to find them! This Wesley did to the best of his ability.

Much of the book is good, sound common sense. For example, 'in extreme fat – use a total vegetable diet. I know one who was entirely cured of this by living a year thus. She breakfasted and supped on milk and water, and dined on turnips, carrots and other roots, drinking water.' Similarly for a fever he urged the patient to 'drink a pint or two of cold water lying down in bed. I never knew it do hurt.' Or, 'thin water gruel, sweetened with honey and one or two drachms of nitre in each quart.'

These prescriptions were considerably less harmful than many of the popular remedies that orthodox medicine had to offer at this time. Wesley's original ideas may have been far from wrong when he advised parents bringing up children to 'let them go barefooted and bareheaded until they are three or four years old at least, no roller or binder should ever be put round their bodies, nor any stays used.' For chilblains he advised a remedy still popular today. 'Apply salt and onions pounded together.' An interesting recipe for 'bleeding of a wound,' is less silly than it looks. 'Take ripe puff balls, break them warily and save the powder. Strew this on to the wound and bind it on.' The finely divided contents of the puff balls would be an effective haemostatic.

Some of Wesley's empirical cures are less savoury and were probably less effective. For instance he advises for consumption, 'every morning cut up a little turf of fresh earth and lying down, breathe into the hole a quarter of an hour. I have known a deep consumption cured thus. In the last stage (of consumption), suck a healthy woman daily. This cured my father.' On 'Raging madness' we see his humanism breaking through for he says that it 'is a sure rule that all madmen are cowards and may be conquered by binding only without beating and that blistering does more harm than good.' Later, however, he suggests putting the madman, 'under a great waterfall as long as his strength will bear,' or 'letting him eat nothing but apples for a month.'

The very variety of Wesley's cures shows the essence of his

Empiricism. He seems to say, 'what may suit one person may not cure another.' Individual 'tailormade' cures must be found for each patient. Empiricism was the very opposite of the cure-all so beloved by the Quacks. If among logical treatments, such as one for a Whitlow, 'a poultice of chewed bread, shifted every day', lies next to a rather less sensible one for 'the whites' (leucorrhea) 'take eight grains of jalap every night for eight days,' then we cannot blame Wesley. Empirical medicine had to experiment to find the best cures available for every disease.

If the 17th- and 18th-century patient found a little difficulty to separate his healers into Physician – Surgeon – Barber – Quack – Empiric – categories, perhaps we may excuse him and yet there was another person available as a potential healer who had been on the scene from the earliest days. This man, professional in his way, was destined to become the nearest antecedent we can find to the average 'doctor' or general practitioner of today. He was the Apothecary. His early days were fraught with troubles as we shall see and it is not surprising in the circumstances, that a large number of this basically respectable profession turned at times to frank 'Quackery' as a way of life.

⚗ 2 ⚗

CURE-ALLS TO THE RESCUE

Of all the Fringe Practitioners we should consider in relation to Quackery the Apothecaries have one great advantage. They, and they only, can claim to have had a reigning British Monarch within their Mystery. King Henry VIII, by the time he took to pharmacy had exhausted most other congenial hobbies and pastimes. But this did not prevent him mastering the Art with some competence. He actually wrote, together with five eminent doctors of the day, a small book on the subject. Many of the 130 or so prescriptions contained in it were 'devised by the King's Majesty.'

The leg ulcers that plagued Henry's later years have fascinated his biographers. The two schools of thought that argue, both quite effectively, on the pros and cons of varicose or syphilitic aetiology will, in all probability never be satisfactorily answered. Whatever their cause, these lesions interested Henry more than anyone else, and a large proportion of his prescriptions were directed towards healing them. 'A plaster to resolve humours when there is swelling of the legs,' and one, 'devised by the King's Majesty to heal ulcers without pain, made with pearl and the wood of Ligni Guaiaci' are typical of many. Unfortunately for Henry, none of the remedies worked and his legs were still ulcerated when he died.

The Apothecary has roots as far back in antiquity as any of the Healers. But he has one great distinguishing feature. He is fundamentally a shopkeeper. In the eyes of our grandparents this would have put him right outside the Professions, into the category of a Tradesman. In most countries Apothecaries were tradesmen of a specialised type. In England they

were at first a kind of grocer. In 1607 they joined with the
Pepperers or Grocers to form the Grocer-Apothecaries Company.
The marriage proved as unsatisfactory as the Barber-Surgeon
liaison and soon divorce was sought. In 1616 the Apothecaries
were granted a charter which formed them into a separate
company. Thus the 'Master, Wardens and Society of the Art
and Mystery of the Apothecaries of the City of London' came
into being.

This looks all very well on paper and would seem to put
the Apothecaries on the same footing as many other City
Companies. To some extent they were just that. They decked
themselves out with Livery gowns 'faced with satin and welted
with velvet,' and bought a ceremonial barge for river pageants.
(This barge was used until 1764 when after an unpleasant
incident in which it nearly sank, the Company ordered a new
boat to be made. The new barge had 'crimson damask coverings
for the back of the master's seat and an occasional footstool
for his use as well as special cushions.' The beadle was also
'reclad in a gown of blue cloth with yellow trimmings.' A set
of new flags and streamers were ordered at a cost of £48).
Officials of the Company periodically searched Apothecaries'
shops for defective or bad medicines and started a rigid apprenticeship scheme and examinations for admittance into the
Art.

With all this very professional activity going on the Apothecaries must have felt themselves elevated from the ranks of
Tradesmen, shops, or no shops. How, therefore, did the faithful
'Potticarii' develop into a near doctor who might be described
as the general practitioner of Quackery? No one has ever given
a complete answer to this question. Several factors were at
work, one of which was the incredibly small number of Physicians
available in England at this time. The anonymous author of
'The Doctor Scarified' wrote in 1727, that a Physician would
appoint a covenanted Apothecary who would not make up his
prescriptions with 'wormeaten superannuated drugs.' But only
one in ten Apothecaries were thus covenanted, the other nine
being compelled to 'sit still or Quack for a livelihood.'

But people had been in the habit of consulting Apothecaries
long before this. It was happening in the 1590's when Robert
Greene was writing his 'Quip from an Upstart Courier.' Greene

knew a lot about the seamier side of life in the 16th century. Dissolution and lewdity were second nature to him. His character, 'Master Velvet Breeches,' who consulted an Apothecary for 'Purgations, pills and clysters,' may have been a self portrait. On occasions 'Velvet Breeches' needed something to boost his flagging and debauched sexuality. Whenever this happened the Apothecary would supply any necessary aphrodisiacs, at a price, 'ten pounds a pint' being mentioned.

From consulting in shops to consulting at home was a short step, and soon the Apothecary was 'going his rounds.' The practising Apothecary was born we know not when, but was well established in the early 18th century. Quoting from *The Doctor Scarified* again, the author includes him with the 'Hackney Physicians and Prescribing Surgeons,' who could diagnose only 'obstruction, consumption and scurvy,' and who would 'remain dumb if these diagnoses were forbidden them.'

Many of these practising Apothecaries were out and out Quacks. But they knew their job well and established their reputation with great care, not neglecting the women folk in their professional attentions. If such a Quack could make a 'true sound on the treble of their (the ladies') fancy, it would produce such harmony,' as would 'sound his Praise through City and Country.' And so, 'in this piece of subtlety, the "Doctor" shows himself no less cunning than the serpent in Genesis who to cheat Adam thought it expedient to flirt to deceive Eve.'

He goes on to say that the Quack by 'opening the other ventrical of his brain,' diagnoses melancholy and intimates to his suggestible lady patient that this is due to her being denied a 'change of Tea Equipage or a new Gown on May Day.' Further, 'he insinuates himself in my lady's favour by spying a small wrinkle or two in the lesser angle (of her eye), and tells her that she has a child or two: and according to the place of the aforesaid wrinkle in the right or left inward angle thence persuades her that in her last lying-in the midwife did not perform her office skilfully, and did not lay her well.' This sort of Quack practice is quite rightly compared with that of the 'Water Gazer and Astrologer.'

Another factor to be considered in trying to see why the Apothecary left his shop to practise fringe medicine, is purely a financial one. Most regular physicians expected their fees to be in guineas, even in the 18th century. An illness of a comparatively minor nature might prove quite expensive. For instance, Sir George Wheler 'caught a chill after dancing,' at a Christmas dinner party. The 'chill' turned out to be 'spotted fever,' and his doctor's bill came to nearly £100.

Many 18th-century physicians made between £4,000 – £6,000 per year. And so patients might feel inclined to call in an Apothecary for minor illnesses. They charged, theoretically, no consultation fee but merely for the drugs supplied. Most Apothecaries' bills were reasonable, three to four shillings being charged for a 'cordial or clyster.' (Enema).

But gradually things changed. Seeing the enormous wealth amassed by the fashionable physicians made Apothecaries jealous. Dr John Radcliffe, whose income was estimated at around the £4,000 year mark, made shrewd comments on why the Apothecaries (and Surgeons) were getting out of hand. He said that 'the Physicians' vast riches in the eyes of the Apothecaries and surgeons, proved seeds sown in their minds that budded into ambition . . . and sharing with them their wealth.' He also stated that 'the neglect and sloth of their masters (the Physicians), had given them occasion to attain (knowledge), as they made them the porters of their medicines to their patients.' The Physicians, he said 'entrusted them with the preparation of their greatest secrets.' Once the secrets leaked out the Apothecaries were in a position to take the patient over, lock, stock and barrel. Radcliffe lamented that a position had been reached, in the 18th century, where the Master Doctor (Physician) comes at the heels of his Man Doctor (Apothecary) to take in hand the work that the Brother Doctor (Surgeon) has either spoiled or could not further go with.'

A description of an Apothecary Quack's activities in the 18th century is as follows: 'Upon his arrival he feels your pulse and with a fixed eye upon your countenance tells you your spirits are low.' He proceeds to prescribe a Cordial which was probably equivalent to our present day tonic. His next question is, 'when was you at stool, sir?' This requires a prescription for a laxative or healing Clyster. Then, 'if besides you intimate pain in your stomach, back or sides, you shall have a stomach Plaister(ointment), etc.' The expenditure to date is 'the cordial composed of some old dusty bill on his file out of two or three musty waters,' 3/6 to 5/–. The Clyster 'made out of a handful of mallow leaves or fennil seeds boiled in water and thickened with rape oil and brown sugar,' 2/6. A Plaister would cost about 2/6.

By the next day the patient should be . . . worse, for 'the medicine of yesterday makes work for another.' And so the Apothecary prescribes: (1) A cordial Apozem, 3/–; (2) A carminative Clyster, 3/–; (3) Another Cordial, 3/–; (4) An hypnotic potion, 1/–. And so, 'thus with the increase of your disease you may perceive an increase of your bill.' On the third day of the illness the patient 'produces an addition of new symptoms and augmentation of the old ones.'

And so the whole prescription is repeated with the addition of 'greater ingredients,' such as 'Magistery of Pearl,' or 'Oriental Bezour powders.' The latter were literally worth their weight in gold, and were priced similarly. By now quite a bill was growing and although this particular parody is exaggerated, many bills in existence at the time ran into twenty or thirty pounds. One particular account for a Mr Dalby of Ludgate Hill lists nineteen items priced at a total of £3 for one day's medicines.

Dr Radcliffe also tells us in a language hardly becoming to a fashionable Physician just how the Apothecary Quacks by their 'bombast, confound and amaze the simple vulgar' (common people). The 'practical Apothecary' had come to see 'a customer, a cobbler that lay indisposed of the cholic, observed him crack a fart, upon which said the Apothecary – Sir, that is nothing but a tonitruration of flatuosities in your intestines. This was no sooner out of his mouth when the cobbler cracked another, and replied – Sir, that is nothing but your hobgoblin notes thundering wind out of my guts.'

The eminent Physician also criticised the Apothecaries for not being well acquainted with the Materia Medica. There is ample evidence that the Physicians themselves were not well up in this subject, for when one Apothecary asked the Physician 'which sort of maiden hair (a herb native to the Mediterranean), was required in a prescription, the Physician replied 'the locks of a virgin.' Radcliffe also said that the Apothecaries provided old medicines, 'their syrups grow acid, their waters are full of mothers,' and 'their electaries and pills are dry and deprived of their most active parts. But you may with as good success preach to a wall as to tell them of it.'

Nevertheless the respectable Apothecary and his rival, the practising Apothecary Quack flourished in London in the 18th century. Many of the Physicians of the day advised them on the conduct of their cases from a fashionable coffee house, charging a half-guinea fee for this service without seeing the patient at all.

One feature of the Apothecaries' practice, and to some extent that of regular Physicians, paved the way for a particular form of Quackery that has appealed vastly to mankind ever since. The idea behind this is easy to appreciate. Clysters, Boluses, Pills, Draughts, and Juleps, were all very well in their way, but they were complicated things. Surely there was some simpler way to get well.

Even eminent medical men like Dr Sloane were still writing in these days prescriptions containing centipedes and millipedes and to make a good viper's broth, took time, care and – vipers. (Take one living viper and remove the head, tail and viscera, excepting the heart and liver. Cut into little pieces and mix it with the blood and add well-water 12 ozs. Put in a closed vessel, boil for two hours and strain, and the broth will be made). In the face of this sort of thing it is excusable that many people would put their faith in a 'cure-all' type of remedy that was effective without being messy. What was really wanted, many thought, was a Panacea. Once the desire was there and the credulity had been expressed it was not long before the Quacks came to the rescue.

The Quack, par excellence, who put 'cure-alls' on the map died in 1761. His name was Joshua Ward. When the *Gentleman's Magazine* of 1762 published his will, many of his patients must have been amazed at his fortune. Doubtless his Quacking colleagues tasted the bitter gall of envy as they read it. Ward's thoughts as he wrote this document give us an insight into his character and background. 'I quit this world with a kind and grateful sense of all those favours conferred upon me by friends and benefactors. I very sincerely forgive all my enemies and earnestly wish that God may pardon their offences as well as mine. It is with humble confidence that I expect to enjoy Eternal Life as the free gift of God . . . I desire that my breathless body may be buried in Westminster Abbey within the rails of the altar, or as near to the altar as may be.'

He left £2,000 to his niece and £500 each to his two sisters, £150 to his personal servant, £100 to his coachman, £50 each to his groom and postilion and several small sums to other servants. To his nephew he bequeathed 'all sums of money he shall be in debt to me at my decease, either by bond or otherwise, and also a £1,000 in money and any three pictures he shall choose.' He directed £500 to be distributed as his nephew and executors thought best. At the time of his death Joshua Ward owned at least four London houses and ran, as evidenced by his will, an impressive retinue.

Previously he had commissioned John Baker, a foundation member of the Royal Academy, to paint designs on his coach. The august academician, 'made a most splendid display of his taste on the panels.' There is no doubt at all that Ward lived elegantly with the élite of England from about 1734 onwards, and died a very rich man.

The cure-all that raised Ward to such dizzy heights of fame and prosperity came in two forms, either as 'the Drop' or 'the Pill.' It did not seem to matter in which form the medicine was taken. The fact that some people just 'can't swallow tablets' is well remembered by pharmaceutical manufacturers today. Ward, as a canny Quack, obviously catered for this disability.

It was during the early weeks of July 1734 that Ward first started to be noticed in London. The sessions had ended at the Old Bailey. Humphrey Hammington had 'received sentence of death for the murder of a V. Clark with a dungfork near Finchley.' Nicholas Balwyn was treated similarly for 'robbing his master of linen to the value of £40.' Four women were also condemned to death for 'coining' (they had all 'pleaded their bellies' but on being examined were found not 'quick'). Five criminals had been hanged at Tyburn one of which 'broke his halter but was immediately tied up again.' At this time over 200 different crimes in England still carried the death penalty including poaching or stealing a loaf of bread.

More exciting to readers of the *Gentleman's Magazine* seemed to be the 'extraordinary advertisements this month in the Newspapers, concerning the great cures in all distempers performed with one medicine, a Pill or Drop, by Joshua Ward

Esquire.' England had heard of Ward before as we shall see. But the scribes writing the *Free Briton*, the *Grub Street Journal* and the *Universal Spectator* probably did not realise that they were to expend many more gallons of ink on Ward's activities before they were finished.

Ward's early days are not very well reported. He seems to have come from a good family, the Wards of Wolverston Hall in Suffolk. He was in business in London in the early days of the 1700's and in partnership with his brother. Together they ran a Drysalter's business, in Thames Street, but the first signs that Joshua was an up and coming young man, occurred in 1716, when he was returned to Parliament as Member for Marl-borough. This was an incredible business as it turned out that nobody had voted for him at all at his election! But Ward's Parliamentary career was halted before it had a chance to develop.

The Journals of the House of Commons for the 20th February, 1716 tell us how the mistake of Ward's election came about. It appeared that 'the right of electing Members to serve in Parliament for the Borough of Marlborough hath for Time out of Hand been (vested) in the Mayor and Burgesses of the said Borough.' The true Mayor had made the correct return of votes in which Ward had a zero score. But one 'Roger William, pretending to act as Mayor though not qualified to do, got possession of the precept and annexed a return thereto of Sir William Humphreys and Joshua Ward Esquire.'

His deprivation of Membership to the House of Commons had little effect on Ward's subsequent career. As Parliament was still sorting out the Marlborough Election he fled to France. It is presumed that he had some share in the Jacobite Rising of 1715. Little is known of this part of Ward's life except that he lived in St Germain and Dunkirk and while he was there 'invented' his famous medicines. Some sixteen years later in 1733, he returned to England taking the precaution of seeking and receiving a pardon from George II before he did so.

Once back in his native land he started advertising his famous cures in a big way. Ward concentrated very much on the upper crust of English society in his early days. He seems to have pulled off some really dramatic cures. One widely publicised was attested by Lord Chief Baron James Reynolds. It must have

been a godsend to Ward's reputation. A young maidservant
in the Reynolds' family, Mary Betts, age 26, had not been too
well for some time and 'after labouring under an ill habit of body,'
she was, 'on Whit Sunday suddenly struck with a dead palsy.'

Various Physicians and Apothecaries treated her without
success in true 18th-century style. Two months after her sudden
illness the 'poor maid was not only emaciated to the degree of a
skeleton, but had entirely lost all muscular motion, insomuch
that whenever she found herself inclined to sleep her nurse was
obliged to pull down her eyelids and to raise them again whenever she was disposed of to wake.' She also suffered from a
total suppression of the menses, 'which even the most powerful
emmagogues could never remove.' In this melancholy situation
she was 'left by the doctors as absolutely incurable.'

Mrs Reynolds had luckily, heard of the wonderful Drops and
Pills. As all else had failed she decided to try them. The results
were immediate if rather alarming. The patient was sick and
sweated profusely. After another dose or two she was 'with
difficulty kept alive.' However, this treatment 'brought down
the menses,' and the maid rapidly recovered and soon, 'dismissed her nurse, dressed without difficulty,' and later, 'walked
about the house and gardens taking the air when weather permitted.' Before long she could 'manage her needle and had a
good appetite and digestion.'

In the 20th century this case would probably be diagnosed as
a psychotic fugue with associated hysterical paralysis, in all
probability occasioned by an unwanted pregnancy. But judging
by the way the case was publicised in the 18th century, Ward's
remedies had worked a veritable miracle.

All Ward's publicity was not so flattering. The *Grub Street
Journal* in 1734 reported that, 'Mrs Gilbert who kept the
Horseshoe Alehouse, Essex Street, of a middle aged and robust
constitution, took one of Ward's pills in the beginning of July
last. It vomited her 34 and purged her 22 times. She sent for an
eminent Physician and Apothecary next day who found her very
feverish, thirsty, having continual retching to vomit, etc.' The
induced gastro-enteritis had 'caused (or at least increased) a
violent navel rupture. The Physician used his utmost endeav-
ours to assist her but could get nothing to pass through her.'
She 'miserably died' during the next night.

This case and eleven others, ten of which were fatal, were quoted by 'MisoQuacks,' a correspondent highly critical of Ward's nostrums. It appears, looking at these old journals, that the whole of London was divided into pro and anti Ward factions. Ward of course was not slow to defend his cure-all. He replied with an affidavit sworn by Jane Clerke, who lived at the Golden Cup in Drake Street. She had been a servant of Mrs Gilbert's at 'the Horseshoe.'

Her evidence was that her mistress was a 'gross, fat woman,' who, obviously fed up with her umbilical hernia, determined to 'kill or cure it.' She had taken previously 'several things from the Apothecary for the aforementioned rupture and found no benefit from them.' Jane went on to say that Mrs Gilbert took the Drop and Pill several times and found herself 'much better for it.' Unfortunately the last time she decided to take her dose she 'supped on a hock of bacon and greens.' This was very naughty of her as Ward supplied with his medicines 'printed directions' which definitely forbade people milk or green vegetables if they were taking the cure. Thus, Mrs Gilbert had contravened 'doctor's orders' and unfortunately she died.

Ward defended the other fatal cases in a similar way. The people who died, he said, were either chronic invalids who were near death anyway, or people who did not follow his dietary instructions. For instance one patient Hester Straps, a barmaid at the 'Bagnio, near Charing Cross,' who had died rapidly after taking Ward's drop, was described by her employer, Richard Haddock, as being in a 'languishing condition beforehand occasioned by hard drinking and irregular way of living.'

One of Ward's most active critics at this time was a Dr Turner. He wrote in the *Grub Street Journal* that Ward's Pill was merely a rehash of a Quack cure popular in London sixty years before. 'One, Russell,' he said, 'a Mountebank, hired a house in Holborn and got from a chemist a preparation like this of Mr Ward's, if not the same, and called it "Panacea." ' He saw the Quack 'moisten this red powder and form it into pills of the bigness of a large pin's head in bulk and colour like those sold by our new Aesculapius ten of which were sold for as many shillings.' Continuing he alleged that Ward's pills were made of antimony salts as were Russell's' and that 'their operation was rough upwards and downwards.'

A lot of this was as we know now, pretty close to the mark. Ward was furious. The *Daily Advertiser* printed his defence of the remedy. He claimed that some 20,000 people had taken the Pill and Drop during the last nine months, and that he was pleased with the progress the remedies had made over the last twelve years. He quoted a decrease in the Bills of Mortality during the year of 3,171 deaths and claimed this 'might have been increased many thousands had my remedies not been made use of.' Allowing for once his pique to get the better of him he avowed that 'as some persons have raised clamours unjustly, he would not for the future give his medicines gratis, as had been his practice, to any person except such as send or come in the afternoon with the certificate signed by the Minister or Church wardens or Overseers of their parish setting forth their circumstances and distempers.' He cannot resist a little quack at the end of this statement, as he adds that, 'those that are deaf, blind or that have disorders of the head must come on Monday and Thursdays, in the morning, fasting.'

A wag parodied Ward's remarks by suggesting that a suitable certificate might run thus:

'We . . . . , the underwritten, do certify that . . . . , a poor person, belonging to the parish of . . . . , may safely undergo a hundred stools and as many vomits without any detriment to the said parish.' Alternatively he suggested, 'We the underwritten church warden of this parish, do hereby certify that . . . . , inhabitant of this parish, is fitly prepared to take the Pill and Drop, and having received the Sacrament according to the Church of England, and received Holy Absolution, and being in Charity with all the World.'

Another correspondent of the *Grub Street Journal* mentioned sarcastically the 'abilities and great success' of Ward being 'too well known among the undertakers and coffin makers and sextons of this City,' and stated that Ward alone had the 'art to kill with one Drop only, whilst others must fill phials and sometimes quart bottles so to do.'

If Ward was receiving a rough ride in the popular press there was no real need for him to be discouraged as his following in influential circles was increasing daily. Henry Fielding then slowly dying of Dropsy, a man who openly deplored regular Physicians wrote, 'obligations to Mr Ward I shall always confess, I am convinced that he omitted no care in endeavouring to serve me without any expectation or desire of reward.' This is a particularly interesting testimonial as Ward had no clinical success with Fielding as a patient and had openly remarked that it was 'as vain to attempt sweating him as a deal board.'

But the most powerful ally that Ward possessed was the King himself. He was fortunate to reduce, successfully, a dislocation of the Monarch's thumb. After kicking him sharply on the shins for his pains, George II became impressed with Ward. He allowed the Quack an apartment in the Almonry office in Whitehall, where he 'ministered to the poor at His Majesty's expense.' The King also gave him a carriage and pair and the unusual privilege of driving them through St James's Park. Royal encouragement made Ward expand his charitable activities. He bought three houses in Pimlico and converted them into a hospital for his poorer 'patients.' This was soon full to overflowing and he bought another house in Threadneedle Street for the same purpose.

Dispensing the Drop and Pill as an act of charity soon became a popular activity among the socialites of the day and it was a common sight to see 'ladies of fashion' distributing the cure-all to all callers at Ward's three 'hospitals.' The Royal patronage was no passing fancy. It protected Ward for the majority of his life. It gave him immunity from the activities of the College of Physicians who would certainly have harried him otherwise. In 1748, when the Apothecaries Act was brought before Parliament to restrain unlicensed persons from compounding medicines, a clause was inserted in it specifically exempting Ward by name from its premises.

As the years rolled by Ward prospered. He now added new remedies to his collection of nostrums, thus repudiating to a certain extent his cure-all philosophy. Turning for a time to a consideration of more scientific activities he patented a process that made sulphuric acid from crude sulphur and salt petre.

When he grew older he devoted himself more and more to charitable work. It may be that the motto 'Miseris Succurrere Disco' painted over the doors of his houses in Pimlico was apt, as even the Annual Register eventually admitted, in 1761, that Ward's houses were 'crowded with objects of charity to whom he always gave with the greatest humanity his medicines and advice gratis, and often relieved them with money.' He seems to have been particularly generous with the latter. The Annual Register of the 17th December, 1759 reported that 'Dr Ward sent this day a benefaction of £50 to a subscription at Slaughter's Coffee House for the relief of the distressed sufferers of the late fire in Covent Garden.' And later that 'near £2,000 have been subscribed by the New England merchants for the sufferers of the late dreadful fire at Boston. Dr Ward alone contributed £200.'

When Ward died he left the secrets of his medicines to John Page who had been kind to him during his early exile in France. He directed that half of the profits subsequently derived from their manufacture and sale should be divided between a home for female orphans and a Magdalen House for reformed prostitutes. The charity was placed under the charge of Sir John Fielding. They benefited greatly at first but when they were 'deprived of the advertisement of Ward's personality,' the profits gradually diminished.

What was the secret of the Drop and Pill? As Ward's critics so rightly surmised the Pill was an antimoniacal preparation. Antimony is not used in medicine at all today apart from the treatment of certain tropical diseases. As a local application it has some value as a counter-irritant, although it tends to produce blisters which often progress to abscess formation.

Taken internally, antimony salts act as expectorants, anti-pyretics and emetics, but they are unreliable in their action and have fallen into disrepute. Over-dosage can produce fatty degeneration of the liver and other unpleasant sequelae. The 'White Drop of Ward' was probably a suspension of am-moniated mercury which acted on the bowel in a similar way to Calomel, a particularly violent purgative. Large doses cause gastro-enteritis, colitis, nephritis and even death from shock and circulatory collapse.

It is difficult to see how such unpromising substances could have enjoyed any success as Quack medicines. And yet successful and popular they were, and even some dozen or so years after Ward's death they were still much thought of as domestic medical remedies. In an interesting little book entitled *The Useful and Entertaining Family Miscellany*, written in 1772, by Mrs Isobella Moore, we find in among a 'collection of above 100 new songs suited to those who delight in harmony, decency and good sense,' and useful advice on 'candying, pickling and pastry,' a receipt for preparing and compounding 'the principle medicines used by the late Mr Ward.'

All a housewife needed for this simple process was a small furnace with a good chimney, 'the fumes would be hurtful to the operation,' a clean iron crucible, a large marble stone with an iron edge around it, 'dragons' blood,' and a 'good stock of rich mountain wine.' A 'fair supply of purest crude antimony' was also required. One cannot help thinking that these are hardly the sort of things housewives would be expected to have in the kitchen even in the 18th century.

A letter Horace Walpole wrote to his friend Sir Henry Moore in 1760 gives a clue which may help to solve the enigma of Ward's successes. Sir Henry had been suffering from headaches and Walpole wrote, 'I don't know what to say about Ward's medicines because the cures he does are performed by him in person. He rubs his hands with some preparation and holds it on your forehead, from which several have found instant relief.' It may have been that Ward's most successful cures were due to the force of his personality rather than the effect of his medicines.

Ward was an impressive man, although his appearance was marred by a large red birth mark on the left side of his face. (He is often referred to in contemporary manuscripts as Spot Ward.) Portraits show that he would have passed as any Georgian gentleman of substance. One allegorical painting of him depicts the healer about to cure a dropsical man hobbling on crutches, a poor paralysed girl carried by her husband, and even a figure depicting ailing Britannia herself. Hogarth, when drawing 'The Undertakers,' however, puts him with his head on Mrs Mapp the Quack Bonesetter's shoulder.

All in all, Ward was a great if controversial character but he may have deserved the epithet:

> 'Before you take his Drop or Pill
> Take leave of friends and make your will.'

Ward was not the first person to do well from an apparent panacea. (Dr Jonathan Goddard, F.R.S., and Medical Professor of Gresham College, a regular physician in his day, made a tremendous personal reputation out of Goddard's Drops. These had a great vogue in the 17th century and Dr Goddard eventually sold the 'secret' of them to Charles II for £6,000. Pharmaceutically these Drops were merely a substance similar in action to sal volatile.) Neither was he the last by a long way. In another chapter we can meet Dr Bossy. He was an interesting Quack in the 18th century but we must ignore him at the moment and examine the activities of his former footman, Dr Brodum.

Corry, writing his *Quack Doctor's Dissected*, tells us that 'Brodum attended Dr Bossy as a footman when that beneficent sage came over to enlighten the eyes of the English. Having obtained the knowledge of several medical terms by being present at the lectures of his eloquent master, this entertaining little lackey resolved to commence doctoring himself.'

William Brodum was, like his master, of German-Jewish extraction. He started his Quack practice in Blackfriars, but success was soon assured and he opened up elaborate premises in the West End of London. Here he sold his cure-alls and could be consulted by 'any lady or gentleman who is exceedingly ill.' They would be 'waited upon with greatest attention for 5 gns. week.' Should the 'exceeding illness' require more attention than Brodum could give as an 'outpatient,' he admitted patients to his house. There, in 'elegant apartments, fit for the reception of any Gentleman or Lady in the Kingdom, with attendance, and use of a carriage,' he treated them on 'terms that meet with approbation.'

The main points of Brodum's Quackery are set out in his two-volumed book entitled *A Guide to Old Age and a Cure for the Indiscretions of Youth*. This was originally published in 1795 and dedicated thus: 'to Youths I write and Virgins uninformed.' Any uninformed virgin reading this book would certainly find it an eye-opener. The first volume is mainly filled with vague medical claptrap of a rather dubious nature, the style of which is strikingly dissimilar to Brodum's other literary 'works.' Possibly ghost writers were active even in those days. Such problems as 'bilious complaints, diseases of the head, diseases natural to women, consumption, asthma, dropsy, and rheumatism,' could easily be cured it was alleged by Brodum's two cure-alls, the Nervous Cordial and the Botanical Essence. To

instantly dismiss any argument on this point well attested
testimonials are quoted, that come from all over the 'Three
Kingdoms.'

This was merely an hors-d'œuvre to Volume Two, which
contains the meat of Brodum's technique. It is addressed to
those who 'have been addicted to practises common to either
sex which are often the occasion of many dreadful disorders.'
Here the Quack really blazes the trail for the more highly
developed sex exploitation Quackery described in a later chapter.
In his way, considering that this was an entirely unexplored field
at the time, Brodum did his nauseating best. While it is probably
not necessary or prudent to quote his 'case histories' in all their
pornographic entirety, the following examples will show what
this 'curer of the indiscretions of youth' could do.

A youth about 17 devoted himself to the seductive practise so
entirely that . . . (he eventually developed), a swelling of the neck,
and a convulsive motion in the extending muscles of the head . . . and
eventual insensibility. After continuing this vice some months he
became exceedingly feeble but nevertheless persisted until he came
to the condition when the evil had made such progress that no medicine
could afford him the least relief. He could not swallow any food, and
after languishing many months he died the most pitiful object. Before
his death he more resembled a corpse than a living man and the
infectious effluvia that came from every part of his diseased body was
shocking beyond comparison.

Brodum implies that had he been called in time things might
have been different.

Apparently not only youths needed the famous Nostrums for
we read later of 'a Captain from the East Indies being on the
point of marriage, who laboured under a dreadful consumption
and was apprehensive that matrimonial engagements would be
detrimental to his health, informed me that previous to his
going to the Indies he had been injured by a venereal disease.'
Brodum almost makes this sound like the honourable scars of
battle but worse is to follow. On examination of the gallant
Captain he finds 'not the least symptom of venereal taint,' but
evidence of 'that baneful habit to which he candidly acknow-
ledged.' This time the Doctor had been called early enough and
the Captain was completely cured by the Nervous Cordial in
six weeks.

The gentle sex was not neglected by Brodum. For instance, 'a young lady from Birmingham' had been addicted to peculiar excesses to such an extent that she 'at length became so weak and emaciated as to be incapable of walking across the room and was at last unable to rise from the chair without assistance.' Luckily she eventually consulted Dr Brodum who cured her with 'two guinea bottles of the Nervous Cordial.'

The confessions of another patient would make most 20th-century teenagers' hair stand on end. She 'fell into practises that she continued until she ran away with her music master at the age of 18. She had four children by her husband in 3 yrs. but they all died as did the husband himself. Unfortunately she then took up her evil practises again until she remarried.' But, alas, now the harm was done and physicians told her that 'her womb was very weak and slippery and that she would have no more children.' After a particularly nauseating description of her physical condition and her sexual difficulties she was, eventually, 'completely restored in a short time to a good state of health' by Brodum.

Apart from the 5 gns. (family size?) bottles mentioned which could 'only be obtained at the Doctor's house,' the cure-alls came in three sizes, priced at £1 2s 0d, 11/6 and 5/5 a bottle. Another modern touch about Brodum is that he advertised the £1 2s 0d bottle as containing 'five times the quantity as the 5/5 one.' (One could 'save' 5/1 by taking the remedy in this way.) The Nervous Cordial was sold in 'flint' bottles. The Botanical Syrup, Brodum's other cure-all, was sold in tin cans, each one had the 'Doctor's Arms,' that is three dolphins and a bear on its label. London residents could buy the cures at eight places scattered about the Metropolis. The rest of England, Wales and Scotland were supplied through sixty odd agencies.

Brodum's activities and the fact that he described himself as a Doctor on the brass plate outside his house, soon brought him before the Royal College of Physicians. Characteristically, Brodum got the better of the President and his Censors. He claimed that he had a medical Diploma from the Marischall College of Aberdeen. When asked how he had got it he replied 'that he had paid for it like others did,' and that his certificate which he produced, 'had been signed by a Fellow of their College.' Strange as it may seem this was quite true. The

Marischall College of the University of Aberdeen, which looks more like a fort than a seat of learning in 18th-century prints, was founded in 1593 by George Keith, 5th Earl Marischall Baron Keith and Altrie. It was not too particular about those to whom it gave its medical degrees, for on the recommendation of two graduates a Diploma was issued without either interview or examination.

The Annals of the College show that 'William Brodum of Mecklenburgh-Strelitz,' received his diploma on the 15th January, 1791, on the recommendations of Drs Saunders and Leo. Later the College discovered that William Brodum was the 'empiric Brodum' and took steps to 'degraduate him' for 'notorious and imprudent Quackery,' and the 'immoral tendency of many passages in his various publications.' The advice of the Solicitor-General of Scotland was sought on this point but he replied that the University had no power legally to expel its members.

The Marischall College, for all its shortcomings, was obviously upset about this and noted in its records that Brodum received his degree due to the inattention of his sponsors. The investigator of the 'debacle Brodum' stated that 'Dr Saunders told me that he was deceived by Dr Leo, a Jew living in his neighbourhood, to sponsor Brodum.' But he 'believed there was no great deception in this case. At least, Dr Saunders appeared to have given himself no trouble in making the necessary examination before granting him the certificate, caring little for the reputation of the Marischall College.'

Many contemporary books hint that the Marischall College would grant anyone a medical degree, guineas rather than knowledge weighing heaviest with the Censors. The following few lines of doggerel emphasise this curious state of affairs:

> 'N'er doubt my pretensions I am a physician
> See here's my diploma and in good condition,
> From Aberdeen sent by the coach on my honour,
> I paid English gold to the generous donor.
>
> If that won't suffice here's my prostitute patent,
> To cure all disease apparent or latent,
> Perhaps you suspected I was but a poacher,
> On the right of physicians a frontless encroacher:

But my qualification's like theirs without flaw,
And I kill my game fairly according to law!'

And so Brodum continued to prosper in London, advertising 'that on each seal of my medicine is the name of Dr Brodum and in each direction is my degree, authenticated by the College of Physicians.' Of course, he had his critics. One went so far as to give a public demonstration of the effects of his much 'puffed' medicines. 'An unfortunate ass was produced to no small amusement of the villagers.' A whole bottle of Dr Brodum's Nervous Cordial was 'administered to the poor quadruped, which on swallowing the dose, brayed most horribly. The victim of Quackery then fell down in a fit from which he was roused by throwing a pail full of water in his face, but had it not been for an emollient drench given by a skilful harrier, the animal would certainly have expired under the operation of the Nostrum.' One old woman, however, who was as 'remarkable for eloquence as her obstinacy,' very judiciously observed that 'the demonstrator had not given the medicine a fair trial, for only a few teaspoons should have been administered at a time.' This was not taken seriously as 'the young people laughed at the idea of an ass being drenched with a teaspoon.'

Demonstrations such as these must have done some harm to the Quack's reputation as did the rather ineptly phrased advertisement that ran, 'a young man of Shoe Lane who has lost the use of his limbs for six months by Dr Brodum's Cordial. Restored!' Most of Brodum's advertisements were quite subtle in their appeal if somewhat crude in their composition. For instance, on 'eruptions on the face,' the doctor deplored the 'inconsistent doctrine of those who recommended external applications for internal complaints.' He asked his readers if the 'fur on the inside of a kettle or boiler will be removed by washing the outside.' His Botanical Syrup, taken regularly for five or six weeks would, of course, clear up the unpleasant condition.

Similarly, an advertisement headed 'Social Happiness,' tells how Dr Brodum's Botanical Syrup procures the health of future offspring. It goes on to state that 'marriage should be the foundation of social happiness, which is often disturbed through parties that form the union, not taking precautions which would secure them the enjoyment of greater domestic bliss.'

Brodum never rivalled Ward in his power and mastery of the art of Quackery, although in his way he was very successful. If Brodum's prescriptions were less harmful than Ward's, his methods of popularising them were unpleasant. He never rose intellectually above his humble beginnings as Dr Bossy's lackey, although he clearly believed himself to be a learned Physician.

𝄖 3 𝄖

THE SPECIALISTS

The mystery of specialisation has always appealed to the general public. This being so we can excuse the Specialists of Quackery sometimes considering themselves a cut above the rabble of the Cure-all vendors.

One of the earliest Specialists was the Water Casting Doctor. An eminent 13th-century physician, Johannes Actuarius, writing *De Urinus*, told his followers that 'the student of medicine has two aids to his work, an exact knowledge of the pulse and a careful study of the urine.' In the Middle Ages a tremendous mystical science was woven around the Urine. Fantastic Uroscopic Charts were devised to help contemporary physicians sort out knotty diagnostic problems. A doctor in the Middle Ages would feel as professionally naked without his urine flask or matula as his 20th-century counterpart would without his stethoscope. But the process of gazing into a flask of urine and diagnosing illnesses was gradually rejected by orthodox practitioners. Once this happened 'urine casting' came as a gift from heaven to their quacking colleagues.

John Halle, writing in the 16th century about Quacks in and around Maidstone, tells of 'one named Kiterell that hath been all his life a sawyer of timber and board, a man very simple and altogether unlearned, who at present is becoming a physician, or rather a detestable deceiving sorcerer. He will give judgement on urines, and while he looks on the water, he will grope and feel himself all about and after a while, where he feeleth, he will shrink as though he were pricked, or felt some pain. Then, he turneth to the messenger and telleth him where and in what sort the party is grieved, while he maketh the people think him very

cunning. They seek him far and near for remedies for such as
are bewitched or enchanted, or as they commonly call it, fore-
spoken. What stuff is this, let the wise and learned judge.'

What stuff indeed – and yet the Quack urine casters continued
to ply their trade well into modern times. An 18th-century book,
The Modern Quack or Medical Impostor, gives the following
advice to would-be patients. 'Whoever hangs out a piss-pot for
his standard, that is the sign of the urinal, pretends upon sight
of your water to tell your infirmities, and direct medicines without seeing the sick person, believe them not. They are cheats:
not only for the sixpence or a shilling for what they call casting
your urine (which much better should be cast in their faces),
but for drawing you in with some fearful story or other of your
danger (they) make you take a packet with you of their stuff.'

The author of this fascinating if rather outspoken book tells of
his personal experience of a Quack who 'made many thousands
of pounds although he could neither read nor write.' This urine
caster having been approached by a woman with a sample of
urine in her flask, put on his conjuring cap, shook his head, and
began very gravely, his 'speech.'

QUACK: This person very bad.
WOMAN: Yes, so he is, doctor.
QUACK: This is the man's water, good woman?
WOMAN: Yes, sir.
QUACK: Here, he much pain in the head? (the quack looks hard at
the woman's face to see if she gives him any line as to how to proceed.
She looks bewildered and he continues).
QUACK: Then here be great pain in the breast.
WOMAN: Very much indeed, sir.
QUACK: Me see here very great disorder in the breast and also in
the stomach.
WOMAN: Yes, sir. He has not eaten a bit of the victuals for this ten
days.
QUACK: He is in the greatest pain in the stomach and the bowels,
the liver decays and the spleen half rotten.
WOMAN: That, sir, is the reason for him crying out about his back,
does it not, sir?
QUACK: Hold! Hold! you do no well to interrupt me what me going
to tell you. This man's kidney is the worse me see this morning. He is
with ulcer in the kidney, great pain, oh, very great pain, poor man.
WOMAN: Truly, sir, so great pain that he cannot sleep night or day.

QUACK: This man be likewise fallen away in the body and in the limbs. This man be very bad indeed, he will fall into the consumption if he do not take great care. But if he take me stuff it will be God's blessing.

This Quack charged a 1/– for 'casting the water' and 5/– for the 'good stuff' he was selling.

Another contemporary observer tells of a Quack who practised urine casting in Moorfields. An anxious woman produced a sample of her husband's water. He had had an accident and the canny Quack noticed the presence of blood in the urine sample, and wisely commented, 'the party hath received some internal hurt.' The wife agreed, but was unsporting enough to press for further details. But she was no match for this expert, who soon found out by means of a few clever questions that the patient had fallen downstairs. The wife asked, awkwardly, 'how many pair of stairs did he fall down?' By now the urine caster having found out where the woman lived, hazarded the guess of 'two pairs of stairs.' But this was apparently his unlucky day, for the patient's wife countered, 'Nay, you are out in your art, he fell down three storey.' Not to be outdone the Quack asked the woman if the sample of urine that he had 'cast,' had been all that her husband had passed that morning. When the wife replied No, she had spilt some, the Quack exclaimed, 'That, woman, was the business that made me mistake!'

The narrator of this tale, once again the celebrated Dr Radcliffe, gave his personal opinion on urine casting in an amusing way. A country woman brought him a glass bottle of urine, very carefully 'corked up,' so that he might diagnose her shoemaker husband's illness. Radcliffe 'poured the urine into a basin then by him and, after he had supplied it with a like quantity of his own, he gave it to her and said, "carry this to your husband and bid him fit me for a pair of boots." ' When the woman said that her husband must first of all take some necessary measurements, Radcliffe replied, 'The shoemaker might as well judge by the urinal the fitting of his leg as me that of his distemper.'

Another speciality of the mid-16th century, was 'looking in on the face.' This was a popular method of diagnosis. A master in this art was a man called Wynkfylde. Contemporary medical opinion labelled him 'an abominable deceiver.' He had a special technique. After looking at the faces of his patients and sometimes casting their urine he would, 'by going a little aside and mumbling to himself,' pretend to have some special diagnostic assistance from the devil. He was a great success, not only medically but in his dealings with women.

During the period in question he had three wives living. 'The first lived very poorly in Canterbury, the second after she knew his wickedness departed from him, and the third that he married at Westminster being a rich widow.' His first wife sought him out in the little Kentish village of Staplehurst, where he was reported to 'fare at his table like a lord.' Finding him ensconced at an inn and, 'served as fine as a prince,' she decided to team up with him as a medical assistant. Wynkfylde sent her to an Apothecary for certain drugs. There was some confusion and the Apothecary asked why the Doctor did not write his prescriptions. An inkling as to Wynkfylde's medical skill is evidenced by his wife's remark that her husband was a 'right Latinist and could write no English.'

The reunion did not last long for Wynkfylde soon left his wife and when she charged him as an adulterer he quickly moved to another parish. But he was shortly up to his old tricks again, spending '£6 weekly on meat and drink, the people resorting to him from far and nigh for he would tell them such wonders that they all had him in admiration. But specially he was cunning to enchant women to love.' A blind man named Ongar lived in a village nearby. His wife was 'sick of diverse aches and swellings.' Anxious to get Wynkfylde to see her he 'sent his daughter for him upon a Wednesday.' Master Wynkfylde so enchanted the daughter that she 'forgot her way home to her father and mother insomuch that her mother thought her lost and she tarried there until the Saturday following.'

Then she decided to go home but, 'being halfway, her mind was so intoxicated that she returned back again to her lover.' By now Wynkfylde was running up an inconveniently large bill at the inn and he decided that it might be better to move on once more. His mistress suggested her parents' house in the neighbouring town. This seemed an excellent idea to the Quack and he soon won mother over with his 'flattering and crafty persuasions.' All was well for some time until eventually the charlatan's past began to catch up with him again, and a warrant was 'sent out to all constables of that hundred,' to bring him

before the 'Worshipful Justices.' Wynkfylde got wind of the
threatened coup and flew. He left his mistress behind, and was
never heard of again.

Some of the most fantastic pages of medical history tell of the
terrible things that can happen to the human frame when it is
attacked by worms. At one time there seems to have been an
international competition as to who could produce the longest
tape worm. Vienna started off with a mere twenty-four-footer.
Paris countered with one measuring thirty-four-point-five metres
and weighing a kilogramme. But, it is alleged, victory was finally
won by a St Petersburg peasant who presented his proud country
with 238 feet of tape worm. Older reports of 800-yarders were
dismissed as being 'erroneous' by writers on this choice subject.

There was even a disease, presumed to have killed such
illustrious personages as Herod the Great, Emperor Galerius
and Philip II of Spain, called 'eaten by Worms.' Gibbon gives
a good description of Galerius dying of this illness. 'His body,
swelled by an intemperate course of life to an unwieldy corpu-
lence, was covered with ulcers and devoured by immense swarms
of those insects who have given their names to this loathsome
disease.' In all probability he was referring to Filariasis.

The artful Quack, always quick to turn the fear of disease into
ready money, exploited the worm extermination market to the
full. Many 18th-century coffee-houses and taverns displayed
advertisements for worm powders in rather the same way in
which their modern counterparts would advertise cigarettes.
Fabulous stories were told of men and women who got into
terrible troubles with their worms. For example, 'Mr Stiles of
the Lock and Key in West Smithfield was practically eaten by a
worm eight feet long and might still have been alive if only he
had taken the 'Exterminator' which is looked upon as rather a
miracle than a medicine.'

Another curious happening must have astounded Mr Stubbs,
the Westminster surgeon, while he was doing a little embalming
job on a 'gentlewoman who had been dead forty-eight hours.'
While he was hard at work on his task the woman's heart leapt
out on the table and out of it he took a worm as thick as an
arrow, with two heads, one like a serpent.' Obviously with
hazards like this at hand Quacks specialising in worm medicines
flourished handsomely.

Almost any disease, epidemic or endemic, had its quota of Quacks who made it their speciality. Scurvy, a vitamin deficiency disease as we know now, was no exception. Numerous Quacks in the 17th century vied with one another for Scurvy cures but judging by the descriptions of some of the case histories quoted in their testimonials, the diseases they were treating as Scurvy included anything from heart failure to insanity. One speciality, the Golden Elixir, sold by a German Quack for curing that 'popular disease the Scurvy,' cured 'Mrs Cock of Whitechapel, a Latin schoolmaster's wife, who was swelled as big as a barrel and voided about sixty stones,' before she was cured of the Scurvy.

Professional jealousy between the Quacks who hawked such cures was high. Often in contemporary handbills it is possible to see with what anger their feuds were conducted. One particularly bitter exchange ended in one of the protagonists stating that to argue logically with his rival was impossible. One might as well try, he said, to 'syllogise with an oyster wench or wrestle with a chimney sweep when nothing is to be expected in return, save foul language and smut.'

A popular diagnosis in the 18th century, vaguer even than Scurvy had been, was Fever. There were Intermittent Fevers, Remittent Fevers, Simple Continued Fevers, Inflammatory Fevers, Nervous Fevers, Putrid Fevers and Yellow Fever to mention only a few. In this age of Fevers galore it is understandable that anyone with a fever cure would be assured of success.

Such a person was 'Lucky Dr James,' who invented his famous Fever Powder sometime during the 1740's. Trained as an Apothecary, James felt his talents were being wasted. Unfortunately, he was short of one commodity necessary for his establishment as a Quack doctor – ready cash. Undaunted he approached John Newbery. On his way to visit his prospective sponsor it is said that Dr James saw a horseshoe lying on the ground as he passed over Westminster Bridge in his carriage. He got out and picked it up as an emblem of good luck and later incorporated it in the design of his armorial bearings.

Oliver Goldsmith describes Newbery as the 'philanthropic bookseller of St Paul's Churchyard.' Philanthropic he may have been but he combined this quality with good business acumen. Remembered perhaps more for his association with Goldsmith and as one of the earliest publishers of children's books such as *Little Goody Twoshoes* and *Giles Gingerbread*, Newbery immediately appreciated the business potentialities of Dr James's invention. Soon the Fever Powder went into production.

It was an instantaneous success, particularly with literary personages. Walpole swore that he would take it if the house were on fire. Goldsmith himself was an ardent supporter of the nostrum, but at last it let him down as it failed to cure him of the Purple Fever from which he died. Many people, Walpole included, alleged that he would have recovered if he had continued with Dr James's treatment instead of reverting to the more regular treatment on the advice of his physician.

Specialists among specialists occur sometimes. When this happens, the therapeutic atmosphere becomes so highly charged that sparks may fly. Smoke, rather than sparks flew or perhaps drifted down Hanover Square, during the dreary November weather of 1891 when a patient sued a Quack organisation for £100. An advertisement in the *Pall Mall Gazette* had told readers in that year that '£100 reward will be paid by the Carbolic Smoke Ball Company, to any person who contracts the increasing Epidemic Influenza, Cold or any diseases caused by taking Cold, after having used the Ball three times daily for two weeks, according to the printed directions supplied with each Ball.'

A Mrs Carhill bought a Ball (10/–, post free), and used it. Strangely enough she caught the 'flu and stranger still sued the manufacturers when they refused her the £100 reward. After a lot of legal wrangling, Mrs Carhill got her money. Her case made history in the advertising world and it is said that every patent medicine copywriter has the words Carhill *v.* Carbolic Smokeball Company tatooed across his chest.

A hundred years or so before the Lords of Appeal were considering this case, London was seeing and hearing about another Influenza cure. It is only a few minutes' walk from the unfortunate Carbolic Smokeball Company's offices down along Bond Street to 22, Piccadilly. Here was the headquarters of a Quack who modestly described himself as 'the greatest philosopher in this kingdom since Isaac Newton.' His name was Gustavus Katterfelto, 'son of the late Col. Katterfelto, of the Death's Head Hussars.'

Initially Katterfelto was not a medical Quack but a sort of pseudo scientific conjuror of a type that was likely to appeal to 18th-century Londoners. He gave 'demonstrations,' in Piccadilly, on 'philosophy, mathematics, optics, magnetism, electricity, chemistry, pneumatics, hydraulics, poetry, styangraphy, palenchics, and caprimantic arts.' The last three subjects are clearly inventions of his fertile mind. As a 'divine and moral philosopher,' he begged leave to say that 'all persons on earth live in darkness, if they are able to see but will not see this wonderful exhibition.'

Not wishing to miss such delights, London's aristocracy rolled up in droves and the *Morning Post* of the 16th September, 1781, reported that 'Mr Katterfelto was honoured this week with the Duke of Montagu, Lords Cholmondeley, Abergavenny and Ashby, General Johnson, Sir J. Stepney, and several other ladies and gentlemen of distinction. Other newspapers reported the presence of many top-flight aristocrats at Mr Katterfelto's lectures on the 'laws of chance, lodestones, magnets, the four elements, thunder, lightning' and that most English of all subjects, 'the weather.' He also gave demonstrations of his own great invention, the Solar Microscope.

The evolution of Katterfelto's medical Quackery is first seen in a *Morning Post* report in May, 1782. 'Last week, seven hundred persons of all ranks and particularly the first nobility, were at the Exhibition Room,' and saw 'physicians and mathematicians express great satisfaction of the Solar Microscope.' Katterfelto also was 'demonstrating insects on the hedges – seen as large as birds – which caused the late influenza.' On June 3rd, 1872, the newspapers reported an astonishing item of news. 'Mr Katterfelto was taken very ill with the very alarming disorder that at present rages throughout this Metropolis. The symptoms were a great weakness of the limbs, a swimming in the head and a shivering of the whole body.'

He consulted, we are told, a certain Dr Batto's works and tried his medicines. 'He found himself cured in 12 hrs. – Several persons have since been convinced of the amazing efficacity of this medicine and now Mr Katterfelto, as a philosopher and a philanthropist, gives public notice that he has prepared a large quantity of the above invaluable medicine, which will be sold (by him only), at the low price of 5/– per bottle, signed and sealed by Mr Katterfelto.'

Later in the same month the Quack composed what must be the prototype of many a medical scare headline. 'Many thousands of persons have been taken ill in the Metropolis for these fourteen days past. A noted philosopher (guess who), has observed and discovered by the Solar Microscope, that at present the air is infected with a great variety of different insects, and much of the same kind by all accounts which were so numerous in the air in Italy in the year 1423, the time of the Plague.'

This sort of announcement did a lot towards drawing public attention to the Quack. The King himself became vaguely interested for it was reported that, 'last Wednesday morning, as the King was taking an airing through many different streets of London he made a stop at 22, Piccadilly and observed the house where Mr Katterfelto exhibits his wonderful experiments and his new Solar Microscope.' Katterfelto frequently made use of this vague Royal interest in his subsequent advertisements. They constantly refer to the imminent visitation of the Quack by the Monarch, this week, next week, or perhaps the week after – weather permitting.

But strangely enough, although Lords, Bishops, and minor foreign Royalty seemed to have been to 22, Piccadilly, the King never honoured the Quack with his presence. Nevertheless, Katterfelto far from being piqued, contrived to pay graceful compliments to the Court at every possible opportunity. For instance, a newspaper reported that 'the King and the Prince of Wales have taken a very great notice of the great respect shown by Mr Katterfelto last Monday and Friday night, in honour of the Prince of Wales's and the Bishop of Osnaburg's birthdays. It was remarked that those nights there was never known a house in London on a King or Queen's birthday so elegantly illuminated as that was: besides a whole band of music playing all the time which entertained the whole neighbourhood.'

While the influenza raged Katterfelto prospered. In 1783 it was made known that the 'great philosopher has ordered from one of the principal coach makers, a Vis-a-Vis on a new construction to be worth £25,000.' This sum, it was stated, had been 'cleared since he began to exhibit his Solar Microscope and his Morocco Black Cats.' This is an early reference to the Cats that were to become part of Katterfelto's stock in trade during subsequent years. He used them in 'electrical demonstrations,'

Stork. A Quack
by Definition

Surgeons as well
as Physicians
eventually had to
take examinations

Wellcome Historical Medical Library

Doctors did not always show a professional disinterestedness

and strange conjuring tricks that fascinated the 'philosopher's' customers in London.

Curiously they seemed to bring him bad luck. The *European Magazine*, June 1783, proclaimed that 'Katterfelto is sorry to find that writers in the newspapers in the last two weeks asserted that he and his black cats were devils. On the contrary he professes himself to be nothing more than a moral and divine philosopher, and assures the nobility and public that the idea rises from the astonishing performances (he gives).' A few months later Katterfelto offered to sell, for a mere £2,500, all his 'philosophical and mathematical apparatus.' He felt that his 'uncommon apparatus would be very useful for a University or large school such as Harrow or Winchester, as many young gentlemen would reap great advantage from them.'

Unfortunately, 18th-century school governors were as unimaginative as many of their 20th-century counterparts and the apparatus remained unsold. Two months afterwards there was apparently still no sale for the bargain was now marked down to £250, with 'various of the best liquid powders and solid phosphorous and a few very fine diamond beetles,' thrown in for good value. Katterfelto carried on with his curious entertainments in London for another year or so, modestly announcing in the *Morning Post*, 1784, that he had 'discovered the secret of perpetual motion, and that members of the Royal family had declared his performance exceeded their most sanguine expectations.'

Towards the end of the 1780's Katterfelto degenerated from a good-class London Quack to a peripatetic mountebank, making short appearances in market towns throughout the country.

He visited Durham in 1790. Described then as a tall, thin man, dressed in a black gown and square cap, his 'travelling equipage consisting of an old rambling coach drawn by a pair of sorry hacks: his two black servants wearing green liveries with red collars.' The latter went around the town blowing trumpets and delivering bills giving details of their Master's performances. These were of a varied nature. Once he set fire to a haystack inadvertently due to an eccentric take-off by one of his fire balloons. He still sold his nostrums and was at one time imprisoned at Shrewsbury, as a vagrant and impostor.

One of Katterfelto's favourite towns was the small seaside

C

village of Whitby. Here he was always very well received and added to his travelling museum of 'natural and other curiosities which was especially rich in fossils, agates and similar products of the Yorkshire coast.' A special trick with which he delighted the local inhabitants of Whitby was the raising of his daughter to the ceiling by the 'attractive influence of a great magnet.'

Katterfelto died in Bedale in Yorkshire in 1799. Perhaps the most valid criticism of him as a Quack was that he specialised much too narrowly. Influenza is a wonderful money spinner for anybody selling bogus medicines. But epidemics occur at irregular intervals and cannot be relied upon to give a steady income. Due to this Katterfelto was forced in the end to go back to conjuring and legerdemain for his bread and butter.

Advertisements issued in his later years show that he still charged the same price for admission to his show as he had done in his successful days in London. It may be that his disappointing career as a Quack was due in some part to a poor business sense. If he could command three shillings for a front seat in Whitby when he had passed his prime as a performer, he could have charged ten times as much in his heyday in Piccadilly. His wife obviously felt that a good business is better than a pseudo-scientific passing show as she eventually settled in Whitby as the wife of a local publican.

A year before Katterfelto died a child was born in Co. Limerick, who was to become perhaps the most famous Quack Specialist of all time. His name was John Long. His father was a jack of all trades in a traditional Irish way, uniting basket making, steward, parish clerk, harness maker, wire-worker, and constructor of winnowing machines, among his many activities. His mother came from rather more aristocratic stock, the St Johns of Limerick. Why she married Long we do not know. But by one of the strange tricks of chromosome permutation young John received the cream of his parents' genetic characteristics and it was soon evident that he was going to be a person to be reckoned with.

In his early youth he followed in his father's footsteps to a certain extent, working as a basket-maker, carpenter and glazier. By the time he was seventeen he had 'thrown aside the chisel and the diamond and confined himself to the pencil,' for he showed an early talent for drawing. Some rich patrons of the arts raised a subscription and sent him to Dublin to be apprenticed to Richardson, the Irish painter and furniture decorator. While he was with Richardson he attended the design and painting School attached to the Dublin Society.

Training finished, some few years later Long returned to Limerick, and eked out a poor living as a drawing master and artist. Some of his harsher critics maintain that he became a house painter. Tiring of this thin living Long eventually left the Emerald Isle to conquer London, 'with a light heart and not burdened with a heavy purse.' He was apparently an attractive young man and having gained something of a social reputation in Ireland he managed to get introductions into one or two respectable houses in London.

He obtained employment as an assistant to Sir Thomas Lawrence, one-time President of the Royal Academy and fashionable Court painter. Although it has been suggested that Long merely swept up the studio after the great man had finished work, there is no doubt that however humble his position was it helped him to obtain an entrée into London society. While he worked as a colour grinder and assistant, he educated himself and got to know the eminent folk who visited Lawrence's studios. To increase his meagre earnings he undertook to do copies of anatomical drawings. These were used for teaching anatomy in many of the London medical schools. About this time he managed to get himself elected a Member of the Royal Society of Literature and also a Member of the Royal Asiatic Society. In later life he always signed himself M.R.S.L. and M.R.A.S.

Just how he started as a Quack is obscure. The *Biographical Index* of 1855 states that, 'in a letter to a friend written in the year 1826 he mentions having successfully treated a carriage painter who was apparently in a decline. The result of this first attempt encouraged him to proceed, and as like all young practitioners he prescribed gratis, he had no want of patients.' This may or may not have been the truth, but the fact is by 1827 he was doing well enough as a healer to finish with drawing and concentrate on Quackery.

Long's speciality was tuberculosis. Consumption was a very prevalent disease in the 19th century. Many a lovely girl or ambitious youth came to an early grave as a result of a decline.

The X-ray as an aid in the diagnosis of tuberculosis was not to be used for another 100 years, and so in the 1820's the disease was diagnosed purely on clinical grounds. Many diagnoses were obviously largely problematical. In other words 'consumption cures' were ideal Quack material.

If Long's choice of a disease was a good one then his method of diagnosis and treatment was a stroke of genius. He invented a substance that had to be rubbed on to the patient's skin. If the patient was fit nothing would happen at all, but if disease was present then a skin reaction occurred. This might be anything from a simple erythema or redness to exudation and even, as we shall see later, superficial ulceration. Long's own words give his theory in a nutshell. 'Disease originates in an acrid humour which in some cases suspends or deranges the functions and in others injures or destroys the structure of those organs on which vital action depends. I possess a remedial agent by the application of which may it be extracted and disease thus removed.'

The skin reaction was therefore explained by Long as being due to the disease being forced out of the body. If the patient did not rapidly recover then more rubbing was necessary. In some cases, as an adjuvant, Long recommended a course of special inhalations. Once the disease process was under control the skin was allowed to heal aided by the daily application of cabbage leaves to the raw area. On these curious remedies rests the whole of Long's success.

His practice rapidly grew. The house that he had been using in Howland Street, Fitzroy Square, was soon too small and he moved to 41, Harley Street. There he spent the rest of his professional life. He had 'rooms handsomely fitted up' and 'suitable establishments for servants and attendants' constructed. In the treatment room there was a giant vaporising machine the size and rather the shape of a piano, with several pipes leading out of it. Here, patients would congregate to have their inhalation therapy as a group, the great man giving encouragement by his presence from time to time. Elegant waiting-rooms matched the grace and polish of his patients and from his sumptuous consulting-room Long was pleased to see Harley Street packed with the carriages of those coming to seek his counsel. He was soon making over £13,000 a year.

As he became a competitor for the cream of London consulting practice, jealousies arose. A vicious smear campaign was launched upon him by the doctors. The majority of the rank and file of the profession took up the cudgels and were soon after his blood. Long wrote, 'had I practised in obscurity I should not have excited the envy of the medical profession. My offence was – that I practised among the affluent and shared a proportion of those fees which gild the pill of the licentiate.' He further stated that it seemed inherent in the medical profession always to 'hunt the poacher,' in their midst, and for 'every pygmy apothecary to raise up in arms' to 'drum him to destruction.' He took some comfort though from Pope's quotation that 'no man deserves a monument who could not be wrapped in a winding sheet of papers written against him.'

If the profession as a whole were united in their condemnation of Long as a Quack, he made matters worse by vitriolic criticism of orthodox methods of practice. Sometimes he came uncomfortably near the truth. For instance he wrote that 'a slight cold or obstruction in a child which its sensible mother would cure in a night, is fostered by "dear doctor" for a fortnight at the expense of some 20 visits, 12 powders, 3 sleeping draughts and who knows how many doses of opening medicine.' He also argued that: 'to a family of five or six children let the surgeon once be called in and the house will become a perpetual private hospital. There is more medicine swallowed in London owing to this present practise than in the whole of Europe.'

Explaining his principles of treatment Long made a point of saying that 'he had not purchased a Diploma from the Colleges of London, Aberdeen, St Andrews, Edinburgh or Glasgow, where such things are sold, in some cases without a candidate being present. To the contrary he had studied . . . and pondered the dull pages of science by the light of his own lamp and perfected his experiments to his own conviction in the solitude of private life.'

Long made one claim that must have attracted many to him. 'I never reduce the strength of my patients. I have no recourse to surgical operations and avoid risking life on any chance or experiment whatsoever. Nor do I make use of mercury or any other poisonous substance. My general practice consists of applications and certain fumigations, so innocuous and gentle in their nature that they may be employed either by myself or

the patients without producing any unpleasant effects whatsoever.'

Before taking on patients who might be tempted to travel to
London to seek his aid Long used to ask for certain details of
their medical history. He would make discreet enquiries from
the relatives about the patient's ability to walk, whether or not
there was swelling of the ankles, if there was any sputum
being produced and if the patient could sleep lying down on either
side or not. On these simple clinical points he could assess how
ill his prospective patients were and whether or not he could
help them.

Most of Long's medical biographers, who could hardly by
any stretch of the imagination be called unprejudiced, state that
Long never treated anyone who was really ill at all. They
allege that he amassed his fortune by treating the fit, merely
pronouncing them ill after his diagnostic liniment had done its
work. There may have been truth in this but there is no doubt
as we shall see that Long took on many seriously ill patients as
well.

The treatment of two sisters, who incidentally came over
from Ireland for Long's cure provided the first case against
him, that the medical profession had been waiting for. The
girls, named Cashin, came from a consumptive family. A brother
and near relative had previously died of the disease. The young
girl, Ellen Cashin, was diagnosed by Long to be in the last
stages of tuberculosis but was accepted as a patient. Whether
she recovered or not no one seems to know.

Her elder sister Katherine was also diagnosed as being
infected, and started on Long's rubbing treatment. Unfortunately she must have been sensitive to something in the
liniment. The skin of her back became very sore and she not
unnaturally refused further treatment. She gradually became
more ill and her back refused to heal. Eventually her mother
called in Sir Benjamin Brodie, Surgeon to the Queen, and one
time President of the Royal Society. The great man professed
no immediate anxiety about the girl's condition, prescribing a
simple analgesic mixture and a saline draft. The following day
she was dead.

At the inquest, despite strenuous pleading by Long's famous
patients, a verdict of manslaughter was brought in and the

Quack eventually stood trial at the Old Bailey. Here once again eminent people 'one of whom during the course of the trial sat by the Judge's side and chatted to him,' gave evidence of the harmlessness of Long's remedy. The jury was not convinced and Long was found guilty of manslaughter and fined £250, 'which sum the convict extracted from his pocket and paid there and then.'

Was Long directly or indirectly responsible for Katherine Cashin's death? Was there a miscarriage of justice? Why was Long's sentence so light? These questions will never be effectively answered. The medical evidence given at his trial is conflicting and often very much biased. Even Brodie seems to have shown duplicity. The post mortem of the unfortunate girl, carried out some days after her death is difficult to evaluate but would seem to substantiate that whatever killed Miss Cashin it was not Long's liniment.

The doctor who performed the post mortem was clearly puzzled. He stated at the trial that the nearest similar post mortem appearances that he had seen occurred in a case of colchicum poisoning. Long himself put her death down to eating excessive quantities of ripe fruit and not following his advice properly. Whatever the verdict is in retrospect the medical profession and particularly Thomas Wakley (first editor of *The Lancet*, Medical Coroner and one time Member of Parliament for Finsbury) made terrific capital out of it.

Long's practice did not seem to suffer much as a result of his appearance at the Old Bailey. Patients still flocked to him. At the inquest on Miss Cashin, a man actually approached Long and asked him if he would treat his wife. This was a curiously macabre incident as this unfortunate woman was also to die after being rubbed by Long. Mrs Lloyd, the woman in question, suffered not from tuberculosis, but from a recurrent throat complaint, the exact aetiology of which was doubtful. The patient's husband entreated Long to attend. He prescribed his usual inhalations and then rubbed her throat and chest with his liniment.

Very quickly, 'a great redness developed, followed by blistering and discharge.' Long had obviously come across another patient with a personal idiosyncrasy to his speciality. He did not seem unduly alarmed, and merely prescribed cabbage

leaves as a dressing. When called in again Long remonstrated
with her for not attending his consulting rooms for treatment.
He advised a further rubbing. The unfortunate woman, 'thought
she could never submit to rubbing again . . . and declined to see
him any more.' A doctor was called in and although he sought
the best medical opinions available, the unhappy Mrs Lloyd
eventually died a month after Long's first treatment.

Again John St John Long was accused of manslaughter at the
inquest and committed for trial at the Old Bailey. The medical
evidence at this trial was so contradictory and uncertain that the
Quack was acquitted. Although when she died Mrs Lloyd had
a most hideous ulcer on her chest, 'from the armpits across the
chest in one direction and from the collar bones to under the
nipples in the other . . . the soft parts covering the breastbone
being black and sloughing,' something other than Long's treatment may have been responsible. When she died her mouth and
throat were extensively ulcerated and this could hardly have
been due to his remedies. Her recurrent ill health before Long
took over may indicate that she was suffering from a blood
disease and the fact that the rubbing led to ulceration which
would not heal seems to confirm this. Long callously dismissed
her death as 'a conspiracy formed to effect my utter ruin.'

This second death must have damaged Long's reputation
because he found it necessary to publish testimonials of an
impressive nature to boost his practice. One, which probably
ranks as the most aristocratically attested document of its type
ever produced reads as follows: 'We the undersigned, having
been patients of Mr John St John Long, and having had his
lotion applied to us, declare that no blisters were ever raised
on us by it, and that we never knew of it producing them on any
of his patients, that the irritation created by his lotion, heals
again under its daily application; that we have used the same on
our faces, hands and chests and that it will produce a discharge
only where disease exists but in no other part. Many of us have
had it in our mouths and swallowed it with impunity.'

The signatures on this remarkable document, some 86 in
number, include nine members of the Peerage, ten eminent
military gentlemen, three clergymen, an Aide-de-camp of the
King, the Mayor of Hertford and other important people of
substance.

A little later Long moved from his speciality to some extent into another field of medical practice. As he said, 'the great power I possess in extracting fluid from the brain, has enabled me to reach the very seat of disease.' His brief excursion into psychiatry was not without its hazards. Long related that when he went to visit one mentally ill patient, 'on entering the apartment . . . he (the patient) endeavoured to vent his rage on me as well as his attendants, and being prevented he gnashed his teeth and muttered the most abusive language. I speedily applied my remedies to his temples, and having removed the inflammation his head cooled and his irritation subsided.'

His success with lady patients suffering from hysteria was particularly successful. He was called to see, 'one young lady of interesting appearance and amiable deportment of manners,' who had been deserted by her lover. Long tells us that she 'developed a most profound melancholy and at length violent and repeated paroxysms of insanity. Physician after physician was consulted in vain. On my arrival I found her exhausted, emaciated, her speech broken and incoherent, frequently mingled with ardent and pathetic appeals to her former lover, beseeching him to protect her.' After Long's remedies she was, 'restored, and had not for the last twelve months, referred in her conversation to the cause of her misfortunes.'

There is no doubt at all that Long had immense success with women. His portrait shows a man with interesting, sympathetic eyes and he looks more like a poet than a Quack doctor. His mouth, well shaped was strong and his elegant sideboards gave his face a definite virility. He obviously dressed well. The flattery that he received from his successful patients probably made him conceited and imperious.

Long was temperate in his habits but was impulsive and quick tempered. His voice, usually musical, became harsh and dogmatic when he was aroused. He never married although he probably had many chances. Even his most ardent critics agree that no breath of scandal ever touched his name. He even broke off a relationship with 'a lady of rank rather than gratify her eccentric wish to have her likeness taken by him in that remarkable costume – no costume at all – in which she was wont to receive her visitors.'

John St John Long, arch specialist Quack of his time, died in the prime of life, aged 36, from the very disease he professed to cure. He probably caught it from one of his patients. On his death he bequeathed his estate to his brother William, together with the secret of his remedy, which he valued at £10,000. Whether the formula ever found a buyer no one knows. But someone took over from him in 41 Harley Street and used similar methods of treatment. He may have possessed Long's secret remedy which was probably merely a simple counter irritant liniment, but there is some doubt about this. One thing is certain. Long's successor lacked the dynamic personality that had made the impressive cures possible. The rooms that once were packed with nobility were soon empty and silent.

Long's sudden death produced a not easily filled vacancy in London's specialist Quack population, but in all probability this was only a temporary loss and before long other bright young men were there to take over his patients.

It is not possible to dwell further on 19th-century Quack specialists, fascinating as they were, but before the end of this chapter it is worth mentioning one facet of specialist Quackery that is still being exploited expertly today. On one page of a book published in 1960 there are two advertisements. Their subject matter deals with the same organ and the same manufacturer is responsible for both.

One preparation, an amazing vegetable flesh former, has an interesting function. According to the advertisement, if it is 'simply rubbed on you will develop a glorious figure.' A testimonial states, 'I have actually developed my bust 4½ inches and my breasts now are a lovely shape, high and firm.' Just below this advertisement a second one tells us about a slimming cream. By judicious use of this 'you can reduce 3–5 inches. Simply rub this harmless cream on to the breast at night, and in a few weeks you will have a youthful, slim figure.' It is tempting to speculate what would happen if you used both products together.

This sort of pseudo-medical hocus-pocus has been going on all through the 20th century. Enormous fortunes have been made out of slimming and fattening nostrums. Some of the best examples of these specialist Quack cures come from America. While the world is full of fat people who want to get thinner, and thin people who want to get fatter, they will probably continue.

Getting fat is generally less popular than getting thin, though nevertheless it has its devotees. So much so that the manufacturers of Sargol, a get fat quick nostrum popular in the early days of this century made some $3,000,000 out of it. The product, manufactured for Sargol by the reputable firm of Parke, Davis and Co., was available in tablet form. These cost just over half a dollar a thousand to make and were sold by Sargol at $25 per thousand.

The advertisements for Sargol were masterpieces of the 'be careful or you will be left out of it' technique. 'Sargol Men' were pictured victorious at tennis and on the golf course. Sometimes they would be seen nonchalantly flexing their muscles on the beach, or hogging all the pretty girls at a party. The ladies too could benefit from this great medical discovery and 'Sargol Girls' were obviously popular when yachting (Sargol days are flesh building days), in the swimming bath or at a ball. As the copy man put it, 'Sargol makes peevish, piqued people, plump and healthy. Popularity and plumpness go hand in hand.'

Eventually the Sargol proprietors were found guilty of a fraud. The claims they made for their product were proved quite fallacious and Sargol was shown to consist merely of various hypophosphites together with a little strychnine.

More successful from the Quacks' point of view than get fat cures that don't work are get thin cures that are equally useless. This may be due to the fact that there are more fatties than thinnies in the world and the former part with their money more easily. Amongst the hundreds of obesity cures that have been available for the last half century, one stands out for particular mention due to the slickness of its operation and clever psychology of its organiser. His name was Cunningham. Before he started on specialist mail order Quackery he graduated through the hard school of fraudulent real estate operation. Cunningham was one of the earliest people to make full use of a personality as a selling point. As his own personality was not a particularly attractive one as far as we can gather, he decided to 'buy' one that was. Her name was Texas Guinan and she was an actress.

Texas, as advertisements tell us, had had trouble. Her theatrical agent had quietly taken her to the door of his office and affectionately shown her out. What was the reason for this discreet but firm demonstration of lack of public interest in Miss Guinan? Had her act been slipping? Was it a question of perhaps a too great a liking for the bottle? Or had she been temperamental at rehearsals? No, the gentle reader was assured, there was not any evidence of these faults in Texas's career. It was merely that to quote her own words, 'in tights I was a sight at 204 lbs (14 st. 8 lbs.).'

This we can believe as she published a picture to prove it. But Texas was not downhearted for long, 'out of chaos came an inspiration.' She tried an obesity cure. Within ten days she had lost 17½ lbs. 'Joy returned,' she tells us, 'I was found dancing before the mirror, singing as a full throated field lark sings at dawn.' Her limbs that had been 'so big and ugly and cumbersome,' had regained their 'lost slimness and beautiful lines and her big bust slowly subsided to its original shape and the days passed like happy dreams.' Naturally she went back to see her agent. He immediately offered her a contract on terms that made her 'eyes stick out.' But she retained, we are led to believe, a great desire to help those having similar troubles to her own, and decided not to return to the glamour of the footlights, but to devote her talents to the easement of the profound psychological suffering of the obese.

The American Medical Association was not wholly convinced by Miss Guinan's apparent benevolence. They also knew Cunningham's background of gaol sentences and bogus patent medicine companies and decided to investigate. Writing somewhat economically to Texas, 'Dear Madam, Please send me your new book that is free, and advise,' they received in reply a letter from which it would seem that Texas was clairvoyant as well as a slimming specialist.

'I am sincerely glad to get personally acquainted with you through your reply to my advertisement,' Texas wrote. 'I am positive it is going to prove a friendship that will result in a world of boundless happiness for you!' The letter continued in the same vein at some length, telling of 'precious new liberty that will be yours after you have been forever released from the cruel prison that has so long held you captive.' Later Texas came to the point. 'I am a woman and in this thing heart and soul, out of the great joy it has brought me both to be slender

and see all others slender . . . so fill out the enclosed guarantee
order and send it at once with 20 dollars . . .'

Soon after this letter arrived at the American Medical Associations's headquarters, Texas wrote again. 'I am puzzled,' she
said, 'more puzzled than disappointed at failing to get a warmly
enthusiastic response from you before now. From the way you
answered my advertisement, I felt positive you were intensely
in earnest in your longing to get rid of your fat.' However,
Texas offered, 'one chance to save ten dollars on the Texas
Guinan positive fat reducer, an order made now would render
your chin, throat, arms, abdomen, hips, thighs and lower limbs
. . . enchanting.'

The A.M.A. resisted the temptation and waited. A third
letter arrived. Texas confided, 'pardon me dear, you may think
me awfully conceited, but I am a bit proud of what great critics
have said about my newly made form. I have in my right hand
the power to give you . . . a pliant, reed-like, form . . . the glory
of youth's lithesome grace.' We are told that the clerk dealing
with this correspondence at the A.M.A. offices was an almost
cadaverous individual. He still remained unresponsive. Texas's
fourth letter lamented that he was still amongst the 'piteous
prisoners of fat, fat girded, fat manacled, fat menaced.' But she
could not bring herself to forget him and blot out the 'awful
unrest the dull desperate unhappiness,' that he must feel. She
offered to send the priceless cure for a mere five dollars this
time, provided he sent her the names and addresses of five fat
men and women of his acquaintance.

Still the fascinating offer fell on deaf ears. Letter five promptly
followed. This was, 'the last offer that will be made to you.' It
asked for the names and addresses of ten fat men or women and
the cure would then be sent for three dollars The money was
eventually dispatched and a quart bottle of muddy liquid was
received. When analysed it consisted of Alum, 1 lb, alcohol,
10 ozs, water to 2 pts. The approximate cost was estimated at
30 cents. Later a Los Angeles Judge issued a fraud order against
Texas Guinan incorporated and this profitable item of Quackery
disappeared from the list of many obesity cures available to the
gullible.

4

EYES RIGHT

A speciality that has not been mentioned so far is Eye Quackery. Perhaps the most thoroughly developed field of irregular practice, it has been graced with some of the highest financial and social rewards. Nobility sometimes lionised the specialists met in the previous chapter, but Oculists enjoyed Royal Appointments. There are two reasons for the popularity of this Quack speciality. Firstly, ophthalmology was neglected by orthodox medicine until a comparatively late date. Secondly the eye more than any other organ in the body has been a source of wonder to mankind. It therefore had great Quack appeal.

The eye is the subject of many curious ideas and superstitions. Popularly believed to be a mirror of the soul, it is thought capable of expressing the emotions of fear, anger and hate, as well as love, joy and sorrow. The belief dies hard that a man or woman with an evil soul is capable of projecting wickedness through his eyes and thereby damaging fellow creatures in some way. While a few people accept today that the glance of someone with the Evil Eye can cause milk to sour, a cow to slip its calf, or even a loved or dear one to die, many were cruelly tortured with the Boot or Rack or burnt at the stake, for just this belief. Numbers of Continental Europeans still accept such fantasies as fact.

The late King Alfonso of Spain had the reputation of possessing the evil eye. When, exiled in Italy, he was invited to dinner by that indefatigable American hostess, Elsa Maxwell, his ex-Majesty found himself the only guest. The Italians, to a man, failed to turn up, fearing contamination. Alfonso's reputation rested on pretty firm foundations. When he had come on a state visit to pay his respects to Mussolini some years previously, several disasters occurred. As the Spanish ships approached Genoa a sudden storm arose and many Italian sailors were drowned.

Eventually Alfonso's ship entered the Bay of Naples. A ceremonial bronze canon was fired in his honour but the ancient gun exploded, killing its crew. Later, after the King had landed, an officer to whom he had been introduced, suddenly dropped dead. A final disaster clinched the matter as far as the Italians were concerned. Shortly after Alfonso had passed by, the Lake Gleno dam burst its banks, drowning many local inhabitants. From then on he was labelled a 'jettatore' and the people jingled keys as a prophylactic whenever he was about.

And so the eye is still thought of today as an object of fear and fascination. Many people dread blindness second only to death. It is no wonder that Eye Quacks had enormous success in their specialisation.

As we have seen, Oculist Quacks hawked their wares all over Europe in Roman times and probably persisted well into the Middle Ages. The first Oculist to get a Royal Appointment was Thomas Clarck, who may or may not have been a qualified doctor. He was 'physician Oculist to King Charles II and King James II, in whose presence he couched a cataract in a lady fifteen years blind and restored her sight in an instant.' Another early operator was George Fairclough. He advertised, 'he hath given such eminent proofs of curing all sorts of Eye conditions late in London.' A handbill of his reported that one unfortunate patient brought to him had been attacked by a burglar. The ruffian had struck him down, 'with a piece of iron, then battered and flatted his face, and twisted his hands in his hair, placed his thumbs in the corner of both his eyes and by a violence forced them out. In this barbarous manner he was brought to me: yet with God's assistance I replaced the eyes and restored him to perfect sight again.'

Most Quack eye doctors did not aspire to such surgical triumphs but specialised in various eye lotions and waters. A Mr Harrison of the Royal Exchange invented a special snuff, 'strongly recommended to improve the eyesight.' This 'Lisbon Snuff' retailed at 23/- lb. Many patent eye lotions and drops have remained popular to the present day. But as Dr William

Buchan said in writing his *Domestic Medicine* 150 or so years ago, 'I have examined many of them and find that they are pretty much alike.' They have another similarity – they are all therapeutically quite useless. Luckily the majority of them are innocuous and merely relieve their purchasers of a little money from their pockets.

Thomas Clarck set the fashion for Royal Oculists. In William III's time he was succeeded by Paddington MacQueen, about whom little is known except that when he died he left a fortune of some £16,000. When Queen Anne came to the throne she showed herself particularly partial to Quacks. Having 'weak eyes,' she singled out the Oculists for special favour and her name is specially linked with that of William Read.

Read started life as a tailor. He was, it is generally admitted, an uneducated man who could scarcely read or write. How he obtained his knowledge as an Oculist remains a mystery, but he practised his arts in the North and West of England for many years before he settled in London in the early days of the 18th century. His headquarters could not have been very imposing as he shared a house with 'Mr Agulters, musical instrument maker, at the sign of the Crown, over against York Buildings, in the Strand.' While Mr Agulters mended musical instruments, Read mended eyes. One of his original handbills in the British Museum tells of the fame of the 'Oculist and Surgical Operator who after twenty-two years of travel and practice hath acquired the true method of performing all curable distempers incident to the eyes, and couching cataracts, glaucomas and suffusions.'

Read also advertised that he 'cured the poor of blindness, cancers, wens, hair lips, wry necks and deafness for charity.' Over the advertisement was a picture of Read operating and several smaller illustrations showed his various instruments.

Whether Read actually treated Queen Anne with any success we do not know. But the monarch was obviously impressed very favourably with him as she knighted him in 1707, 'as a mark of Royal favour for his great services done in curing great numbers of seamen and soldiers of blindness, gratis.' Marlborough's march on the Danube and the subsequent heavy battles which took place, probably brought streams of wounded troops into London. Read persistently advertised that he would continue to treat sick soldiers and sailors for nothing as long as the war lasted.

Once he had been accepted by the Court, Read rapidly moved up in the world and lived and entertained in the company of such men as Steele and Swift. He kept a sumptuous table and used golden vessels to serve drinks to his guests. He published a book, presumably written for him, that is unremarkable in its contents. Its only merit is that it probably did a lot to stop unpleasant and harmful remedies being used in eye doctoring. For example he was against putting 'the juice of goose dung or the white part of hens dung into the eye.' He also did not approve of 'licking the eye with the tongue or smothing it with a gold ring.' A popular cure for weak eyes in those days was to 'drink a large draft of beer in the morning.' Read felt this erroneous as he stated that, 'I am persuaded that thousands have drunk themselves blind by this practise.'

When Read died in Rochester in 1715 his wife, Lady Read, took over his work, and we can gather by this that the clinical acumen of this Royal Quack was not particularly high. Lady Read did not go down at all well with Queen Anne. She rapidly transferred her ophthalmic affections to Robert Grant, a Quack who started life as a cobbler and graduated to his profession after a short spell as an Anabaptic preacher. He appears to have been a more rapacious Quack than Read and boosted his celebrity with many forged testimonials.

Both Read and Grant seemed to have held some sort of respectable reputation in their day, although there was criticism of them in the *Spectator* and elsewhere. But on the whole they were accepted as Fringe practitioners of some value to the community.

The last great Oculist that we shall consider differed from them in one respect. Although he possessed a medical degree, in spirit he was an out and out Quack and widely criticised by the large majority of his contemporaries. John Taylor was born in 1703, just before Read was knighted. He was the son of a Norwich surgeon, and studied under Cheselden at St Thomas's Hospital. Returning to Norwich to practise, he found that he was not cut out for general medical life in East Anglia and decided to become an itinerant Oculist.

Taylor's career is a fascinating puzzle to try to unravel. On the face of it all should be plain sailing. Two books on him, both fairly rare now, are available for reference. One, *The History and Travels and Adventures of Chevalier John Taylor*, is an autobiography. Taylor styled himself the Chevalier, and the book although interesting is so pompous and self-laudatory that much of it must be taken with a pinch of salt. The other book, *The Life and Extraordinary History of the Chevalier John Taylor*, was published in the name of his son, but was probably the work of the drunken Irish literary rip, Henry Jones.

This 'Life' is a direct opposite to the Chevalier's now account of himself. A lot of it is unpleasant and frankly obscene and would not pass the censor today, but some of the supposed exploits of the Chevalier, bitterly satirised in this account of him, are somewhere near the truth. In all probability between these two 'Histories' lies the true man.

Henry Jones tells of Taylor's early days as follows. 'Between the hours of eleven and one of the 16th August, 1703, did nature and the midwife give our matchless hero to the world. He no sooner began to distinguish objects than he expressed the greatest aversion for all spots either on garments or the countenances of those that came near. Patches, worn on the face, being then the fashion, he often scratched off, and sometimes brought blood along with them – nay he even put some eyes in danger.'

Of Taylor's early professional days in Norwich the critic is typically scathing. He tells of an 'old, rich Quaker, within a few doors of him taken ill with cholic. Our young Oculist was summoned to his relief. Tabitha, the Quaker's newly married spouse happened to cast a savoury leer at our handsome, spruce doctor. The doctor administered to her in all simplicity of heart . . . one fatal morning Ebenezer (the Quaker), came hastily into his wife's apartments, and there surprised the guilty couple. But the doctor gave an early specimen of that address and dexterity which so strongly marked the character of all his future ventures. He claimed that his business there was only to cut his wife's corns. The Quaker, crying out 'murder,' the doctor springs downstairs, at one leap, and scampers up to London.'

Jones goes on to tell of many amorous and perverted pleasures that the young Oculist enjoyed while he was in London working as an Apothecary's assistant. He would have us believe that

Taylor's companions at this time were thieves, whores, paederasts, and body snatchers. Just how much of this is true it is difficult to say, but the bare facts of the History seem substantial.

The typical address that was referred to in the preceding paragraph is a characteristic which differentiates Taylor from all other Quacks. If some of his colleagues show a tendency to blow their own trumpets, Taylor blasted on his as loud as possible. On the title page of his book, he refers to himself as Ophthalmiater Pontifical Imperial and Royal to the King's of England, Poland, Denmark and Sweden, the Electors of the Holy Empire, and numerous other Princes of Royal Blood throughout Europe. He advertised that he was the author of forty-five works in different languages and – that he possessed the 'greatest practice in the care of distempered eyes as any in the age we live – who has been in every Court, Kingdom, Province, State, City and Town of the least consideration of all Europe without exception.'

These statements are a curious mixture of fact, half truth and lie, characteristic of all the Chevalier's writings. It is a fact that on the 3rd September, 1735, 'the famous Oculist, Dr Taylor, was presented to the Queen at Kensington and had the honour to kiss Her Majesty's hand in consideration of his surprising capacity in the service he possesses.' It is also right that he was appointed Oculist to King George II the following year. But it is less true that he was the author of forty-five works in different languages, although he was a prolific writer about himself.

The claim that he was Ophthalmiater Pontifical is probably a direct lie. Taylor's alleged conversation with the Pope would seem to be enough by itself to crush this extravagant assertion. Here is Taylor's description of the meeting:

POPE: I can see to read without glasses. Would you be sorry all eyes were like mine?

TAYLOR: I should be very sorry.

POPE: How?

TAYLOR: Because though heaven gave you good eyes that you might see that all was right: yet the same providence made me what I am, and knew that I must live: and I hope that your Holiness will not blame me for praying for my daily bread.

POPE: These things, my son, concern this world only.

TAYLOR: It is for this world only that I have said these things, for here is my present business.

Taylor's incredible bombast is seen best in the orations that often preceded his clinical sessions. He harangued the crowd in what he called 'the true Ciceronean prodigiously difficult and never attempted in our language before.' Difficult it may have been to the Chevalier but more difficult still for those listening to it as the following example shows:

O Ye! Imperial: O Ye! Royal: O Ye! Great Masters of Empire: who have so far extended by benevolence as to be witnesses of my Labours, when from before the Dark Eye, by my hands the dismal veil was removed. You, the Rulers of Man, point out, as it were with the Sceptre in the Hand, Me alone amongst all Mankind for these things. O Ye! Empress, O Ye! Queens, etc. . . .

Similarly in an address to the University of Oxford, he started,

The Eye, most Illustrious Sons of the Muses, most learned Oxonians, the Eye, that most amazing, that incomprehensible, that miraculous Organ, the Eye, is the Proteus of Passion, the Herald of the Mind, the Interpreter of the Heart, etc. . . . etc.

Examples of the Chevalier's opinion of himself are too numerous and similar to quote any further except that the following few sentences seem to sum up the position as he saw it. Speaking of his talents he asks: 'Shall virtues like this pass unrecorded? Shall it be said that a prodigy like this has breathed within our walls, and that we forgot to inform posterity? No, it must not be. Let us tell our children's children that such a man we once had among us!'

The Chevalier's early days before he received the Royal patronage in 1736, are shrouded in mystery. He toured Britain staying a few days in market or country towns, performing his cures and moving on quickly before unsuccessful cases had a chance to catch up with him. According to Henry Jones, who wrote his satire it is said from notes supplied by Taylor's son, 'he travelled northward like the sun giving light and joy at Newcastle and elsewhere . . . in Scotland.' After an alleged, 'bigamous attempt . . . Edinburgh became too hot for him and he scampered off for Ireland, lands in Dublin and is well received.' But here, 'he meets an unfortunate rub. A young gentleman under his care, had by his own misconduct, in getting cold, and an inflammation in consequence, lost the use of one of his eyes. He was a member of the University, and a person of family.'

According to the chronicler Taylor was invited to the unfortunate patient's house, ostentatiously to have a consultation with several learned Physicians to see what could best be done to put things right. Taylor agreed and, 'dressed in a suit of rich velvet,' was led into a darkened room. Here there was no patient or doctors, but hooded figures who danced around him chanting ominously, 'Oh, Taylor, Taylor, give me back my eyes.' After this eerie demonstration they tied the Chevalier's legs together and hoisted him up to the ceiling. Then, placing a burning brazier under his head, tortured him in no uncertain manner. Later a print was supposed to have been distributed in Ireland showing the oculist dangling over the coals.

Just how much truth there is in this story no one knows, but judging by the number of times it was alluded to in various parts of the 'Life' it may well be factual. Between 1727 and 1736, Taylor travelled widely in Europe. He talks blithely of his cures and social successes during this period. Jones merely tells of the many amorous adventures with sundry European lady friends more suitable to an Erotica than a Biography.

After George II officially accepted Taylor there is more factual information available about his activities. A letter written by a certain John Palmer in January 1747 gives an account of the oculist in action at Northampton. Taylor apparently operated in the mornings and lectured in the evenings. 'The doctor appeared dressed in black with a long, light, flowing tied wig: ascended a scaffold, being a large table raised about two feet, and covered with an old piece of tapestry, on which was laid a dark coloured chariot seat with four black bunches (used on hearses), tied to the corners for tassels, four large candles on each side of the cushion, and a quart decanter of drinking water to moisten his mouth. He bowed, snuffed the candles and descended to the company, and delivered out his handful of syllabuses. Then mounting his scaffold he bowed very low: then, putting himself in a proper attitude began in a solemn, tragical tone.'

A picture of Taylor on tour in continental Europe, in the 'crisis of his grandeur,' tells of him 'travelling in an impressive manner with two coaches and six black horses, five of which were blind, due to their master's experiments.' His entourage consisted of ten servants and a gentleman companion. On arrival in any town of merit Taylor would rapidly distribute elaborate personal advertisements. These described him as 'an Englishman not addicted to drinking and without a pre-conceived flattering opinion about his Nation.' This apparently endeared him to the local populace who were then pleased to consult him. His success is shown by the fact that in Amsterdam 170 people sought his advice in one day, and Taylor had to be protected from the exuberant enthusiasm of his patients by a Civil guard. The Oculist made a great parade of his 'instruments of glimmering gold, his portfolio of testimonials and a striking collection of 200 pictures of eye diseases, painted on glass and copper.'

At home Taylor was not always so well received. At Canterbury, once, his stage coach was mobbed by the representatives of some ungrateful patients. But it was in Scotland that Taylor really found the natives unfriendly. In 1740 an anonymous work published under the pseudonym of 'Sartorious Sinegradibus' sat'rised Taylor unmercifully. The following example from the book shows what Scotland thought of the Chevalier.

Great births are frequently attended with extraordinary circumstances of omens and dreams: so it happened to the doctor, whose mother while with child of him, dreamed she brought forth a nine-eyed eel, which sliding through her hand, dived into the mud never to be seen . . . The doctor while an infant, being obliged to eat great quantities of crabs' eyes, was thought then to have contracted that voracious appetite for devouring eyes which has never been satisfied since.

Later the doctor with an indefatigable and never enough to be admired industry, collected a sufficient quantity of the aqueous, vitreous and crystalline humours of various animals, and mixed them in due proportions and made a vow to use no other drink . . . Besides this thin diet, the doctor indulged himself often eating the coats of eyes, ophthalmic herbs, which he dressed with butter of antimony and cream of tartar. At the same time he began to powder his wig every morning with sublimated mercury from which he felt great benefit.

His mother was now glad, it is said, to find the doctor suitably occupied and he quitted 'throwing stones at neighbours, poultry, riding the minister's cows on the grass, pissing in milk-

pails, and flinging ashes into the potage by way of salt.'
Instead he spent whole days and nights grinding down knives
and needles and even 'bleeding the cat in the temporal arteries
and jugular veins.'

The satire goes on to tell that as an experiment Taylor, 'cut
a piece of flesh out of his own buttocks and having taken the
eyes of a favourite dog of his mother and brushed them clean,
he put them in the holes, dropping a plaster of burgundy pitch
over them to keep them in until they should take root. Then, not
wishing to lose any of his own flesh he fried the two pieces he
had cut out in butter and ate them that evening for supper with
spinach and eggs.' After this extravaganza the author gives an
account of what the Chevalier undertook to perform.

1. All weak and tender eyes that cannot bear the light the doctor
undertakes to manage, so that in a few days a greater light shall not
affect them.

2. All the eyes of old people not under 150 years old the doctor
undertakes by a simple operation to make see as well as they did at
fifteen.

3. All those who delight in optical observations and have frequent
cause to shut one eye, may repair to the doctor who at a very incon-
siderable expense, will save them the trouble of shutting that eye for
life.

4. The doctor makes an eye to any character that is desired. If a
gentleman would appear gallant he shortens the musculi amatoris so
that he should always be ogling. If a lady would pass for devout he
makes the eyes be continually turned up, a young officer fierce, he
makes them stand out, a politician's eye he makes turn every way at
once.

5. For the use of all wives with hard-hearted husbands, the doctor
teaches the art of brewing tears that will melt the hardest marble or
flint.

6. The doctor takes out any gentleman or lady's eyes and having
turned them outside inmost towards the brain, the said person shall
afterwards see ideas passing in their own minds as clearly as they
would any object in the brightest sunshine.

As a final blast against Taylor's Quackery his lampooner
alleged that 'the doctor has a very fine oil which being injected
into the eyes, and set on fire while a room is darkened, the
smoke conveyed by the lacrymal duct through the nose makes
the prettiest appearance imaginable.'

Later many Scottish newspapers criticised the Chevalier. *The Scots Magazine*, June 1744, quoted 'we have of late had very ample accounts in our newspapers from one Dr John Taylor, designed Oculist to His Majesty, who has resided in Edinburgh upwards of two months, of his own extraordinary knowledge and success in the cure of diseases in the eyes. But the Incorporation of Surgeons published an advertisement in which they represent the doctor as the very reverse of what he pretends to be.'

The Edinburgh Royal College of Physicians also had something to say about the Chevalier. 'Whereas one John Taylor has inserted in the newspapers of this City, several advertisements, stuffed with gross injurious falsehoods, we, the President, Censors and Fellows of the Royal College, in justice to the public, and in vindication of our character, do unanimously declare that: (1) Not one of the Professors of the different branches of medicine in this University ever attended one single lecture of his (Taylor advertised that the College professors attended his lectures out of educational motives); (2) That some of our number who were present out of curiosity, reported them exceedingly trifling.'

The notice went on to say that members of the College who had seen Taylor's operations found them unremarkable and attended with indifferent success. The College also alleged that Taylor demanded exorbitant fees, often for small services and threatened law suits if his accounts were unpaid.

Some five years later Taylor's name in Edinburgh was not much sweeter, for an announcement of his return to the city was given immediately after the reports of proceedings in the Circuit Courts. The Justices had found May 1749 a heavy session. We read that, 'six men were carried from Cromar to Aberdeen for wearing the Highland habit,' and imprisoned for seven weeks. Three were hanged for horse and cattle stealing. Three surgeon apprentices were indicted for grave robbery but did not appear and so were 'fugitated for noncompearance.' A sexual offender was brought to justice. 'One John Hudd, a hecklemaker, from Pleasants, Edinburgh, a married man was tried before the sheriff of the Shire for seducing, plying with liquor and then debauching, seven young girls.' Later he was sentenced to be kept in the Tollbooth for six weeks on bread and water and then 'to be whipped by the common hangman at the nine usual whipping places in the City, to receive five lashes on the naked shoulders at each and be banished from the Shire.' The 'bawd, who procured him the girls,' was caught and 'accordingly they were both whipped together.'

The announcement that 'Dr Taylor, Oculist, is now on another tour,' followed directly upon this somewhat startling account of how Edinburgh dealt with lechers in the 18th century. The proximity of these two reports is too close to be accidental, especially as it continued 'for the gentleman's character we refer to the declaration published by the College of Physicians in 1744.'

If the Chevalier's reputation was unenviable in Scotland, elsewhere it was probably better. Many continental doctors refer to him favourably. A French surgeon said that his 'hand was as light as it was sure.' In Germany opinion generally was that Taylor was a clever operator but too 'liberal with his promises.'

Dr Lecat of Rouen saw Taylor operate on a squint. He 'took up a fold of conjunctiva by means of a silk suture, cut it off and then clapped a plaster over the sound eye.' When Lecat asked the Chevalier about his technique he was informed that to weaken the overpowerful muscles causing the eye to squint, a 'nervous filament of supply must be cut.' Taylor promised to teach the Frenchman how to do the operation and demonstrate the nervous filament. But Lecat soon saw through the quackery and eventually got even with Taylor. Entertaining the Chevalier to dinner he had a dish set before him. When the cover was removed it showed 'a human head, cleft from forehead to neck and carefully dissected as to the eyes.' Lecat asked Taylor to show him the illusive nervous filament, but for once the Quack was struck dumb with horror and could demonstrate nothing. The whole incident is interesting because Taylor seems to have stumbled on the treatment of squint by operative procedures.

Taylor also attempted plastic surgery. Apparently he had some success although we only have his own word for it. However, the following account rings true. A patient had her lower lid distorted by a burn of the face in such a way that part of her eyelid was prevented from closing. Taylor dissected the skin off from the muscle surrounding the eye. The patient repeatedly shouted, 'you hurt me, you hurt me!' but the Chevalier put her on her mettle by answering, 'remember Lady, Beauty! – Beauty!' and on this she kept her courage. Afterwards when Taylor presented her to friends, 'they were astonished and it looked as if the business had been done by some miracle.'

Another successful cure occurred in a patient who apparently suffered from ptosis. She 'was obliged to throw her head back or raise the eyelids with her hands if she wished to see.' Here Taylor removed part of the upper eyelid and then drew the edges of his incision together operating rather in the same way as a surgeon would today.

Taylor's most startling cures were those that he performed on the blind. He was adept at treating cataracts. There is historical evidence that the ancient Egyptians operated on cataracts and so there was nothing particularly new about it in the 18th century. Cataracts, in which the crystalline lens of the eye becomes opaque, can cause blindness if they are bilateral, unless treated surgically.

The methods of dealing with cataract have varied over the ages. In 1705 Brisseau wrote a treatise in which he showed that the couched cataract was merely the lens pushed back into the vitreous humour that lies in the posterior part of the eye. A better method than couching cataracts is to remove them en masse. This is broadly speaking the operation done today. But technically it is more difficult. Jacques Daviel, Oculist Surgeon to Louis XVth, was probably the first person to remove cataract by extraction in 1749, but it was some years before he decided that this manoeuvre was superior to the older operation.

An account which, strangely enough, comes from Edinburgh, written in the middle of the 18th century, gives a good idea of Taylor's technique of couching. 'Taylor makes a small puncture with the lancet through the coat of the eye in the ordinary place of piercing with a needle in this operation,' the report tells us. After testing the cataract to see if it would separate, the operator, 'introduces his needle and ruptures the cataract along its lower edge and then pushes his needle down into the vitreous humour of the eye.' Then he 'thrusts the altered crystalline out of the aperture already made in the lower parts of its capsule,' and finally, 'brings his needle back and pushes the cataract into the divided part of the vitreous humour.'

The medical observer who wrote this account thought Taylor's method efficient but unremarkable. It probably had a fair degree of success and may well have given sight back to the blind.

When Taylor published his book in 1761-2 he obviously meant it to have a wide appeal outside the medical profession. For instance he related that while in Germany he met a 'young lady whose heart was so tender as to want no spiritual aid to grace her proceedings: and was so successful in a little affair of gallantry as to find her labours had not been in vain.' The Chevalier tells us that the girl's father was not at all pleased with the news and showed it in 'ill becoming terms to his beauteous daughter.' Later, when the baby was born the girl, 'through fear of the infant's proclaiming its arrival by its little voice, resolved in her distress to close its mouth, but continuing the experiment too long the baby gently gave up the ghost.' When the girl's father arrived in the room she called to him, 'with great composure . . . "Father, behold my child – you are the murderer." '

It is impossible to say just why Taylor thought this type of incident would interest prospective patients. Elsewhere in the book he tells us that he had been instructed in the secrets of 'that respectable Tribunal named Inquisition,' and that he had been present at an Auto da Fé. Somewhat proudly he boasts of assisting at the ceremony of 'burning the Jews and other people that had dared to think different from the Established Church.'

He was also, he wrote, 'well acquainted with the various punishments for different crimes as practised by every nation,' and digressed at some length on the Knuet, the Padlock, and the Strapard. In the latter the criminal was tied by the arm and raised to some height on a pulley. The rope was then released so that the prisoner would fall as far as possible without actually hitting the ground before the rope tightened. This, Taylor explained, 'dislocated his shoulders and was sometimes followed by lameness for life.' The Chevalier also details his personal knowledge of methods of execution all over the world. These ranged from the conventional beheading or breaking on the wheel to more complicated methods such as 'walling up.' In all probability Taylor felt that such bloodthirsty accounts would impress his patients and also raise him in their opinion in some way or another.

In summing up Taylor, Man, Quack and Oculist, it is necessary to bear constantly in mind the standards of morality and medicine that prevailed nearly two hundred years ago. Physically by all accounts he was an attractive man. His face was handsome and his bearing haughty. When he chose he could make himself charming. He was obviously very much intrigued with women. The picture painted by his biographer may have been over-drawn but the Chevalier was a man who dallied considerably with the fair sex. In his own 'History' Taylor makes frequent references to women. For example, 'I had the happiness to be personally known to two of the most amiable ladies this country has produced, namely Lady Inverness and Lady Mackintosh, both powerful figures and of the most pleasing address, both sweetest prattlers, the prettiest reasoners, and the best judges of charms of high life that I ever saw. When I first gazed on their beauties, etc.' The Chevalier published a book in Italian on *The Art of Making Love with Success*. Unfortunately there now appears to be no trace of this epic volume. Taylor claimed that he had a flair for 'reading women,' and that there was 'no lady living this side of forty but on fixing my eyes upon her I can read her very soul.' Exactly what he means by this is equivocal.

Taylor's experience of women was not confined to the secular. He was particularly partial to nuns and said that 'these beauties surpass ordinary women in the language of love, wit, vivacity and sublimity of thought because they are always meditating on these things.' Elsewhere he mentions that he had been into every 'female nunnery in Europe.' (On professional visits of course). The nuns of one convent demonstrated their 'wit' on Taylor in a way that he did not appreciate. Instead of his professional fee they gave him a statuette of the Virgin.

On the credit side it must be admitted that although Taylor was only an average operator and often resumed peregrinations before the results of his surgery could be fairly judged, his knowledge of the anatomy and physiology of the eye was far in advance of many contemporaries. He also had a facility for making prognostications about eye surgery that have been subsequently proved true. His theories on squint are a case in point.

In later years Taylor picked up a mass of practical knowledge in ophthalmic surgery. An instance of this was his advice to leave unilateral cataracts alone, as he said, 'where there is a cataract in one eye and the sight in the other eye is good, the patient don't ought to be encouraged to suffer the diseased eye to be couched, because symptoms which may possibly attend it may be the occasion of the loss of both.' He was referring to the condition well known to ophthalmic surgeons as 'Sympathetic Ophthalmia.'

Chevalier Taylor's chief enemy was his own bombast. He also took undeniable liberties with the truth. An example of this is the allegation that he operated on and cured Bach of blindness when he was in his eighty-eighth year. In this case he had unfortunately forgotten that Bach died blind at the age of 75.

Another unpleasant side of Taylor's character was his method of insinuating himself into the favour of eminent people. One of his letters preserved in the British Museum shows a particularly smarmy approach to Sir Hans Sloane, then at the height of his fashionable fame. The letter itself, ill-composed and poorly executed probably did not have the desired effect on Sloane although the famous Physician thought it worthy of preservation. Perhaps he kept it to check up on whether the testimonials enclosed with it from important medical men such as Mead and Arbuthnot, were genuine or not.

With all his bombastic quackery Taylor had a lively wit. Once when dining with some barristers on the Oxford Circuit and having treated them to his usual self-laudatory performance, he was asked, 'Pray Chevalier, will you be so good to tell us anything you cannot do?' 'Nothing so easy,' replied Taylor. 'I cannot pay my share of the dinner bill, and that, sir, I must beg you to do.'

As he got old, Taylor, suffering from poor sight himself, found patients harder to come by. He finally left England in 1767 and died in Prague in 1772. His son John Taylor II, who was trained by the Chevalier, practised independently, and more professionally than his father, in a house in Hatton Garden. When Taylor senior died, the post of Oculist Royal was not transferred to young John.

George III appointed Baron de Wenzel his Oculist but on the Baron's death he gave the honour to John Taylor II, who held it for the rest of his life. His eldest son, John Taylor III, was subsequently made Oculist to George III and George IV.

Thus we have three generations of Taylors appointed to three generations of the British Monarchy, a tribute of Royal favour that has never been equalled in Fringe medicine to this day.

Even with Royal favour on himself and his family the ultimate verdict on the Chevalier must be a critical one. His biographer said of him, 'the doctor could as soon be satisfied with one woman as with one guinea. He was never happy but when, like a comet, he was stared upon. He was an epicure in idea only. His table, like his clothes, was meant to be gazed upon and he would un-button an eye as easily as he could his waistcoat.' These few terse lines probably sum up the Chevalier as well as anything that has been written about him, although some may prefer to accept Horace Walpole's doggerel as an accurate assessment.

> 'Why Taylor the Quack calls himself Chevalier,
> 'Tis not easy a reason to render,
> Unless blinding eyes, that he thinks to make clear,
> Demonstrates he is but a pretender.'

5

THE MEDICAL INSTITUTES

No one would expect cacti to grow in the back gardens of Manchester. Or brussels sprouts in the Sahara. The climate would just be wrong. Everyone knows that environmental factors have a profound effect on animal as well as plant life. The huge monsters whose skeletons impress and bewilder us in the Natural History Museum probably died out for the simple reason that their prehistoric environment changed to such an extent that survival was impossible.

The human animal can compensate by means of his ingenuity and intelligence for considerable changes in his physical environment. But changes in psychological environment are more difficult to cope with. Scientific knowledge and factual education have altered public opinion and popular beliefs to a surprising extent in some ways. This has sometimes caused a way of living to disappear completely. A wet nurse would have precious little chance of finding a position today but only fifty or so years ago such people were very much sought after professionally.

To understand some aspects of Quackery it is necessary to recreate the environment in which they existed. America at the turn of the century was an exciting place. The effects of more efficient mechanisation were beginning to be felt and the country was growing rapidly. Immigrants were flocking in from Europe and Asia. The cities, particularly coastline ones, and those around the great lakes, were bursting with young men determined to be 'going places.'

A stroll along the waterfront of such a city would be a surprising experience to someone from the 1960's. The docks would berth several masted sailing ships, their long bowsprits pushed out over the quayside. An occasional power-driven vessel, often a paddle boat, would be seen but these were generally speaking in the minority. The paving of the quaysides was probably wood blocks, which felt curiously soft to walk upon but which were treacherously slippery when wet. On the wide sidewalks, sometimes concreted, but often planked and raised considerably higher than our modern pavements, hustled the noisy throng of young America.

Ships' chandler's shops, where one could buy a good rope, knife or rifle, were next door to Chinese laundries — often centres of illegally run lotteries. Clothing stores, specialising in the heavy duty type of garment necessary for a seafaring community or for pioneering activity in the country, sometimes had a large secondhand section for the less pecunious. Noisy bars, almost exclusively catering for men, butted on to cheap cafés and flophouses of various types, where twenty-five cents was considered a lot of money to pay for bed and breakfast. If a house advertised 'rooms to let,' it usually turned out to be a brothel which might well be sited right next door to the chapel.

Often the most prominent place in the district would be where loungers congregated around a penny arcade. These establishments were similar to the amusement arcades seen in many of our seaside towns. Burlesque shows specialising in striptease or other amusements of a very 'broad' kind were probably much in evidence. The noise of an out of tune piano mingled with sounds of ships' bells, and the shouts of draymen. Advertisement hoardings jutted out at almost every angle from the buildings. A huge pair of gilded spectacles announced the office of an oculist. A barber's pole vied with a real estate advertisement for attention. A vendor of 'New American Rambler Bicycles' might be seen competing with the wares of the 'Premier Buggy Company,' advertising the Phaeton selling at 85 dollars. This was the very latest that could be had in modern transportation.

Perhaps around one small store window a crowd of men would collect. These men might be young immigrants, fresh off the boats, sailors, weary after a long commission, perhaps a little jaded after a few nights on the town, or maybe countrymen up from the backwoods to sample the delights of the city. A closer look would show them to be peering a little anxiously

Polypharmacy
in embryo

Wellcome Historical Medical Library

Apothecary Quacks came under fire from Rowlandson

Katterfelto was not alone in discovering perpetual motion

Perkins at work on a True Briton

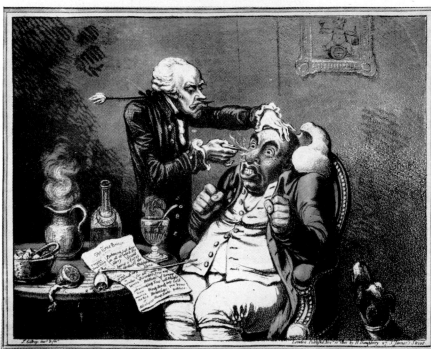

at what was going on inside. Let us look over their shoulders for a few minutes.

In the shop window two figures can be seen. One of these is a bewhiskered gentleman wearing a pince-nez spectacle attached to the lapel of his black coat by a silk cord. His high winged white collar rides well over his black cravat. There is something professional about this man. Yes, of course, he is a doctor. He is crouching over the other figure in the display who lies on the floor. His face turned towards the window, has the deathly pallor only a waxwork achieves. His clothes are awry, he has weed between his fingers and in his hair. He is obviously dead, or dying of drowning. The doctor's hands rest on his patient's back, as he kneels just over him. Suddenly, quite slowly and rhythmically the doctor moves backwards a little and his hands leave the man's chest. There is a moment's pause. He then replaces his hands and leans once again over the unfortunate patient, whose chest moves slightly under the pressure. A ghastly mechanical wheeze is heard. After a few seconds the whole manœuvre is repeated. The audience is rapt, perhaps half hypnotised by this recurrent and of course unsuccessful attempt at artificial respiration.

Over the shop window in letters perhaps a foot high is the word 'Museum.' A sign-board invites the public to walk in. Admission is free. Should the entranced window gazers have needed further incentive to lure them into the 'Museum,' it was usual for the first few 'exhibits' near the door to be 'anatomical' in the frankest way. Few young men can resist the lure of pornography particularly if the subject purports to be of an educational nature. One soon steps inside. Passing on from the voluptuous waxwork ladies, the models become less attractive physically but certainly not less interesting. As a matter of fact they mostly showed the havoc caused by that most sexual of all hazards, venereal disease. Primary chancres of the sexual organs and elsewhere on the body were depicted in hues worthy of technicolour. Syphilitic rashes and sores, nasty as they are, could seldom have been depicted uglier. The later effects of the disease, ulcerated noses and palates, gummatous ulcers and paralyses were all shown in realistic detail. Even the model of a nurse and doctor caring for a poor, wretched syphilitic baby were not forgotten. The lesser venereal danger, gonorrhœa, was

D

not neglected, of course, but did not lend itself to illustration quite so effectively. The waxworks merely had to content themselves with strictures, arthritis, and blindness!

Another supposed terror of the age was not omitted from the show. Masturbation was widely believed to cause almost everything medically, from boils to baldness. The young man wandering round the museum may have felt sure in his own mind that he had no risk of developing any of the terrible syndromes demonstrated to him, but on the subject of masturbation he was probably not so confident. The proprietors of museums realised this and exploited it in the following way.

In a prominent place at the back of the museum a dark cabinet was situated. Shattered and yet curious to see just one more exhibit the visitor presses his nose against the glass. Perhaps he thinks the light has failed and that this last horror is going to be forbidden to him. Then suddenly the case is illuminated and facing him, less than three inches from his nose, is a leering, idiot boy. His irregular teeth grin in his drooling mouth and his glassy eyes roll hideously in their sockets. The light is just brilliant enough to read the title of the exhibit. It is 'LOST MANHOOD.'

Unless our potential customer is a pretty tough nut he staggers back, completely unnerved by this last exhibition of what can happen to a young man who is not pure in thought, word and deed. But as luck will have it a kindly and yet professional looking figure approaches him and asks him 'is he all right?' Perhaps he would like a glass of water, or to sit down. This man is the 'floorman.' He has been watching our young friend and has already summed him up as a 'live' one. After he has made his offer of refreshment or rest, he soon gains the young man's confidence.

Within a few minutes our shattered customer has confessed that he is worried. The floorman's reaction is not reassuring to say the very least. The comforting look that was on his face when he fetched the glass of water has gone. Now he looks grave. 'You know, your symptoms sound serious to me. Why don't you come upstairs and see our specialist. He'll soon find out what's the trouble and it won't cost you a cent. The consultations here are free!' With this he ushers our young friend upstairs with perhaps his arm around his shoulder in a brotherly way. The 'live' one has now been 'hooked!' And in the technical language of the medical institute is a 'rummy.' The first act is over, the second one is about to go on.

Our young if rather indiscreet American has stumbled upon what may generally be called a 'Medical Institute.' These organisations, using in many cases a 'Museum' as a shop window, were commonplace at the turn of the century. Some were small one-man shows. Others were well organised big businesses making handsome profits.

The institutes that did not use the wax museum technique, advertised extensively in newspapers and handbills in the best traditions of old-fashioned quackery. Many of them had impressive names, such as 'The Advanced Medical Science Institutes,' 'The Electro-Oxygen Institute,' 'Interstate Doctors,' 'The Radio Medico-Electro Doctors,' and last but not least 'United Doctors.' They were usually staffed and financed by non-medical personnel, carrying some person or other with a registrable qualification somewhere in the United States, as a professional 'cover man.'

The activities of these institutes were just as immoral as a Museum-front Institute. They tended to concentrate less on the venereal side of medicine, however, and were merely clip-joints for the credulous and unwary, who did not want to, or could not put their faith in the hands of a reputable practitioner. A lot of their custom came from claiming that by means of a special process they could cure such ominous conditions as Cancer, Bright's Disease, and Tuberculosis. Eventually, of course, the news got around that they did not cure anyone of any serious disease. This gave them rather a peripatetic background and they tended to open and close their 'offices' in various towns from time to time at short notice.

The Museum-type Institutes relying mainly on the 'private and secret' diseases peculiar to men were on a more certain wicket. Disappointed clients were unlikely to complain. The institute in which our imaginary 'rummy' or 'boob' (to use the slang of the institutes' employees), goes slowly and apprehensively upstairs, was probably one of the thirty or forty establishments owned by the Reinhart-Flint organisation. These were the most efficient and well-run of many similar 'houses' and produced tens of thousands of dollars for their organisers.

The floorman who so cleverly hooked his 'rummy' had been specially picked for the job and had gone through a short apprenticeship or training. The Reinharts liked young multilingual men with pretty heavy family or financial commitments who were temporarily down on their luck. In a cosmopolitan community the former qualification was a distinct advantage. The latter factor proved useful in holding down a man who might be inclined to 'talk' when he had learnt the ropes.

During his instruction he had to learn how to talk reasonably and intelligently about the hundred or so exhibits displayed in the museum and learn how to 'hook' the potential 'boob' so effectively that he could not escape. The size of the floorman's salary was proportional to the number of customers he could persuade to go upstairs. The average floorman was expected to produce about eight new patients a day. He was instructed not to pass himself off as a Doctor and yet grow a beard and cultivate a 'professional manner.'

Once upstairs the floorman showed his charge into a small waiting-room, saying that the specialist or doctor was busy but would see him as soon as possible. Within a few minutes he came back, in a new guise this time, as a 'case taker.' He produced a form and in fact took a fairly detailed medical case history from the poor 'rummy.' The history probed well into the patient's sex life and gave the 'specialist' plenty to work on when he eventually saw the patient. This completed, the floorman prepared to carry out his final and yet very important task.

From the moment that he saw the patient entering the museum he was sizing him up from the financial point of view. He may, of course, have previously seen the 'rummy' about the town. Many floormen would make it their business to know the clientele of most of the local brothels and bars. A good floorman would not waste time on anybody with an empty pocket. But the ultimate test was yet to come. Before this all else was conjecture.

The history taken, the patient was asked to undress before seeing the doctor. Then, when he was eventually shown into the doctor's consulting room the floorman made his final assessment, in the most efficient way. He went through his wallet! Within a few minutes the result of his search and his case sheet were on the 'Doctor's' desk. The 'men's specialist' was now in a position to examine, diagnose, prognosticate, and treat. From all reports the type of examination the unfortunate 'rummy' received was rather varied. In some institutes weird and wonderful machines were connected up to the patient before the diagnosis was made. More commonly a routine physical examination was made.

There exist in the files of the American Medical Association many first-hand accounts of such consultations. The doctor would be initially cheerful and start off in a routine way, exuding confidence and platitudes. As he progressed a little in his examination his cheerful manner would evaporate. Serious trouble had apparently been discovered. After a few minutes on the 'hot seat' the patient was told quite positively and confidently that he had a serious disease, usually syphilis or gonorrhœa. If the quack had seen from the history that such a diagnosis was patently impossible then he would probably content himself with diagnosing varicocele (a fundamentally benign condition as we know now), seminal weakness, or prostatitis. Sometimes a blood test would be suggested to confirm the diagnosis, or the urine might be 'analysed.' As these Quacks had usually no facilities for either of these tests the fate of any specimens taken was probably the kitchen sink.

Now, diagnosis made, and prognosis indicated, the next job to be done was 'feeing the patient.' This process, to use the colloquial term of the medical institutes, was started as soon as possible after the initial shock of the diagnosis had been experienced. The whole business of diagnosis and 'feeing' is well illustrated in a case reported in the *Chicago Tribune*. A reporter had posed as a patient to a notorious quack 'men's specialist.' After he had been examined the doctor enlarged on the diagnosis.

'I am sure you have prostatitis, you have sugar in the kidneys. I don't want to say how much until I have a sample tested in my laboratories. It is too late to do that today. You have an ulcerated urethra. You might have posterior gonorrhœa. I am inclined to believe that you have. I don't want to tell you today just how serious your case is, but it is something that will require a long treatment, but I can tell you, you had better come here again Monday and as often as you can afterwards.'

'I can't come every day,' the patient protested. 'Would every Saturday do?'

'That would be fine,' the doctor rejoined. 'Now we will have to make some arrangements about the bill.'

'What will it cost me?'

'It will cost you 100 dollars for a cure. You may be worse than I think you are and it may cost you more than that. You have a long road to travel. I will have to build you up for some three to four weeks before you will be able to take the treatment for your kidneys.'

'When will you want the 100 dollars, doctor?'

'Well, I don't ask for payment in advance, but I want a deposit. I would like fifty dollars down, anyway.'

'Doctor, I came away in a hurry and I didn't bring much money with me.'

'I can't take less than 25 dollars.'

'But I haven't got that much.'

'Pay me ten dollars, then.'

'Doctor, all I have is five.'

Needless to say the doctor pocketed this fee which was credited on a small card. Here the interview ended. The reporter, who had posed as a patient for this consultation, was a young man of twenty-five, six feet tall, weighing 185 lb., and an active football player in the prime of life. He was not much dismayed with his harrowing interview. For the sake of veracity his newspaper arranged for a check medical to be carried out. He was of course passed A.1.

The same technique was followed in the Reinharts' Institutes. The results, in a business sense, were phenomenal. Only one person suffered, the poor wretched patient. The Quack would fleece him of every cent he had. and often actually sued for fees, having got their patients to sign 'iron-clad' promissory notes for treatments on credit. It is not surprising that such frauds would have many unpleasant sidelights to them.

Drs Kennedy & Kennedy of Detroit fell foul of the law when they became mixed up in a suicide case. A typical Kennedy & Kennedy advertisement ran, 'Reader, Are you a Victim. Have you lost Hope? Are you intending to Marry? Has your blood been Diseased? Have you any weakness? – Our new method of Treatment will cure You. Consultation Free!'

One young immigrant, reading such an advertisement, began to worry. He consulted the Kennedy doctors who told him that his worst fears were true and that unless he took treatment he would live only a few weeks. They had the only treatment that would cure him, they said, and he must pay 150 dollars in advance, or they would not take his case. He had no money and could not borrow any. He had only one course open to him. He took a revolver and shot himself dead. A post-mortem examination proved that he had nothing wrong with him at all! As a result of this case one of the partners spent sixty days in the Detroit house of correction and the other one fled the country. Similar cases quoted in the American Medical Association reports did a lot towards the eventual stamping out of this vicious practice by completely unscrupulous Quacks.

The particular brand of quackery seen in the American Institutes, existing as they did in an atmosphere of general scientific ignorance, could only be countered in one way. The general public had to be informed of their follies and educated medically to the extent that they would no longer swallow medical hocus pocus, hook, line and sinker. The latter would take some time, the former could and was eventually tackled as we have seen by the newspapers.

One method of exposure was to get 'floormen' to talk. Once they started there was no stopping them. Having been sacked from an Institute for one reason or another and given anonymity by the newspapers, the 'secrets' of treating secret diseases soon leaked out. One of the Reinharts' men is worth quoting at some length.

'The work was pretty easy,' he said. 'Most of the visitors were young fellows from the country. A large percentage were not sick at all, only thought they were, as a result of a guilty conscience. I'd talk to them for a while and then stick some disease on them. I had a list of diseases. The virulence of the disease depended on how much money the sucker had. If he had lots of it I'd tell him he had syphilis, and show him by means of the wax figures that he was developing the symptoms. One fellow had a wart on the side of his hand. I convinced that chap that he was in an advanced stage of syphilis, simply by comparing his wart to a wart on one of our wax dummys.

'After I had convinced him that he had the disease I took him upstairs to the chamber of horrors and showed him what he would be like in a week or two if he didn't take our treatment. I didn't have any pangs of conscience about skinning these 'boobs.' Most of them had a skinning coming to them the way they had been acting, and I figured that anyway it would be worth the money to them if we did throw a scare into them that would keep them out of trouble in future.

'But a little later in the day I ran across several patients that worried me. One of these was a poor devil with cancer. I knew by looking at him that the best doctor on earth couldn't cure him. Another fellow was so weak with T.B. that he could scarcely walk. I went through the motions and got them up to the doctor. Without batting an eyebrow our Quack told them he could cure them in a month. This went on . . . all the time I was getting sorer and sorer on my job. The "blow-off" came when a nice young chap came in and said he had hernia (Ruptures have had a slightly disreputable reputation until quite recently.) He had been to see another Quack, who had injected paraffin wax into him. He was going to get married and wanted himself "fixed up."

'I knew by then what our doctor would do in this case. He would take out the first lump of paraffin, and inject another one in its place.' To cut a long story short when the unfortunate fellow was eventually 'fee-ed' the sum of 25 dollars, he could not afford to get married anyway. Curiously enough this seemed to upset the conscience of our 'floorman' more than anything. He 'felt ashamed' of himself, and ventured to say to the young patient, 'Clear out of this place and don't come back. These fellows are a bunch of robbers.' He was unfortunately overheard in his advice and instantly fired.

Another floorman gave the following eye-opener of life behind the scenes in a Medical Institute. 'One day the buzzer sounded upstairs and we waited a long time for the patient to appear. When he didn't show up I looked down the stairs and there was Compton almost carrying an old man up the stairs. We got him into the consulting room. He had neither hair nor teeth, he was deaf and his sight was failing. Compton had talked him into the belief that the only reason he was not as young as he used to be was because he had lost his manhood and that we were the only people who could restore it. He signed a contract for a course of treatments. Of course we got the big

Wellcome Historical Medical Library

Lady Doctors like Lady Quacks were often
unkindly criticised

Cholera Quacks
complete with
protective
clothing and
nostrums

initial fee, which ensured his return for more treatments. We had to carry him downstairs on the way out.'

He continues later, 'I mixed the prescriptions. We had several types of medicine that looked impressive. Most of it was coloured water. The doctor would write a prescription for Aqua Missourionus (Missouri River water). Our popular "come-back" prescription was for Elixir-Simplex. It was almost pure whisky and any man can get a jag on it.'

One day, apparently, the doctor had been drinking the Elixir himself and had left one of his electrical machines switched on. It burnt out during the night and a young mechanic was summoned to repair the wiring. The 'floorman' had a small bet on with the doctor that he would 'get' the mechanic as a patient. He succeeded. Proudly he reminisced. 'I got Potter. He didn't know that he had anything, but before I got through with him he was convinced that he had gleet (gonorrhœa). When we used to joke about it afterwards we would say, "Well, if he has not got it he might get it. You can't tell!"'

Reports such as these appearing in local papers together with the activities of the American Medical Association eventually persuaded public opinion of the dangers inherent in consulting bogus doctors who lurked behind 'Museum' fronts. Not all the Medical Institutes were quite as bad as the ones we have examined. Some of them quite possibly did some good.

One quite unique organisation is worth studying. It was the Lesley E. Keeley Institute at Dwight, Illinois. Dwight, as a town had a poor beginning. It was named after Henry Dwight, a Chicago business man who financed the Chicago-Alton and St Louis railroad. In July 1854 the first train ran over the new line and Dwight was then little more than a telegraph pole with a tin pan nailed on top, which had served as a landmark to the railroad surveyors. Unfortunately the new line was not an immediate financial success. As a matter of fact poor Henry Dwight rapidly went broke over it. But, telegraph pole or not, he gave Dwight his name before he 'retired' from the railroad business.

The new line did not make much of Dwight, however, for until 1890 to quote the *Chicago Guide*, it 'slumbered along as a sort of community of retired farmers, and apparently knew as little and cared as little of the outside world as the outside world knew and cared about it.' It resembled a 'frontier village,' we are informed.

And yet within three years Dwight was thriving. The railway company had erected a handsome granite station. Huge loco-motives, each complete with cow-catchers, bell, giant headlamp, not to mention tall, vase-shaped smoke stack, brought at regular intervals large numbers of visitors to the growing town. Six hotels were opened up (rates, 3 dollars a day and upwards). An express office was started, and a newspaper, *The Star & Herald of Dwight*, was being published. A new post office coped with the difficulties inherent in a community in which some 1,500 visitors might come and go in a single month and whose letters might well be addressed merely 'Dwight, Illinois.' Dwight had become a minor boom town. Boom towns always owe their fame to some local discovery, oil, diamonds, silver, gold, or more recently, uranium. In Dwight's case it was gold – bichloride of gold – to be precise.

The discoverer was no hoary-handed prairie prospector. He was short, dapper, moustached Dr Lesley E. Keeley, M.D., L.L.D., previously railroad surgeon of the Chicago & Alton. The story goes that Keeley's father and grandfather, both physicians, sought during their lifetime a cure for drunkenness. Where they failed their son, who was practising around Dwight in between his duties as a railroad surgeon, succeeded.

To quote a journalist of the day, 'one night the student walked forth from his laboratory. Dwight was asleep: the late trains had passed: a quiet joy filled the student's heart. Why? He was satisfied that the long sought remedy had been found. A strong test was not long wanting. Shortly afterwards Dr Keeley was summoned to attend an old man who had attempted to commit suicide. He was the village drunkard. The doctor saved his life and then applied his discovery. The old man lived many years but never took another drink of liquor.' This is a difficult bit of journalese to swallow, but 'quiet joy' or not Dr Keeley quickly exploited his theory, allegedly based on the properties of bichloride of gold. Soon, trainloads of visitors were arriving at Dwight, turning the sleepy hamlet into a 'gold-rush' town. Drunks from Chicago, St Louis, Indianapolis, Cincinnati and Detroit turned up in their hundreds.

Dwight, or rather Dr Keeley, with his staff of M.D.'s and

other ancillary workers, was ready for them. Some of the visitors might arrive drunk at the handsome granite-built station, and would fall off the train into the arms of one of the doctor's attendants. They were instantly given a hypodermic injection in the left arm and started off on their first two-hourly dose of the Keeley remedy. The attendant was also provided with a four-ounce flask of 'good whisky' so as his charges should not suffer unduly.

One point about the Keeley treatment was that the drunk was always weaned off his drink in the early days of the treatment. This minimised withdrawal symptoms such as delirium tremens which might have otherwise occurred. On the first day in Dwight 'an extreme case,' and there certainly seemed to be a good many of these, might be allowed twelve ounces of whisky a day, the next day eight ounces, and next day four ounces. He was always allowed alcohol if he applied for it but in modified doses.

Once on his feet the patient was allowed the freedom of Dwight. He was, however, subjected to a strict code of rules and regulations. They were as follows:

1. No patient accepted for less than a period of three weeks' course of treatment. All patients are required to register and arrange ALL financial matters with the treasurer on arrival. Borrowing or loaning money between patients is positively prohibited.

2. Strict regularity must be observed in the use of the remedy every two hours during the day and promptness at the office for hypodermic treatment four times a day.

3. The remedy for internal use is compounded to meet individual requirements and all exchanging or loaning between patients is interdicted.

4. The use of tobacco in any form is prohibited for fifteen minutes before and after office treatment.

5. Cigarette smoking and gambling will be punished by instant dismissal.

6. Baths are prescribed twice a week.

7. Patients are requested to preserve silence in the office, while in line, or when through office treatment.

8. Gentlemanly deportment is expected from all, and profanity, lewd conversation, boisterous conduct on the street or at the hotels or boarding-houses will be severely reprimanded and if persisted in will be visited by prompt expulsion.

9. Strangers visiting Dwight, as well as residents, must not be annoyed in any manner: and graduates should be permitted to take their departure without unnecessary demonstration.

In other words you paid your money and you took your cure. The laboratory where the bichloride injections were given was an imposing place. Nine or ten steps led the patient in through two 'Norman' arches to the inner mysteries of the Lesley E. Keeley Company. Once inside the vast waiting-room, lit by half a dozen hanging chandeliers, patients could see employees of the company sitting behind a metal grille rather like the tellers in a modern banking house. The checking of records and the organising of treatments was carried out in this Holy of Holies. Here patients would form a queue and eventually receive their injections, either 'through a slit in his shirt or sometimes with his sleeve rolled up.' Dr Keeley or one of his qualified assistants always gave the injections. If it was the Doctor himself, they had to mind their P's and Q's. Something of a straitlaced individual, he abhorred the use of slang. One word of slang was allowed, however. The Americanism 'shot' was used instead of hypodermic injection, but, we are told, woe betide any patient who called the treatment hall the 'shot tower,' or 'shooting gallery.' Instant dismissal might well have occurred.

Treatment was carried out until Dr Keeley was satisfied of the patient's cure. Keeley claimed a 90 per cent cure rate for those that stayed the course. A graduate, probably wearing the badge of the 'bichloride gold club' that was provided for the patient to wear, as a 'shield and reminder,' is credited as being the author of the following eulogy. 'I am going home next week to let my wife get acquainted with me. We have been married twelve years and she has never known her husband. Such sunshine as this, has fallen on thousands of households that were once desolate, but are now filled with happiness. This is why strong men break down in tears when they come to say goodbye. They have formed acquaintanceships which are different from any they made before and which are the blossom and fruit of a common knowledge of sorrow and common bitter experience. To the jaded brain the song of the thrush and the call of the robin come with new meaning as the man finds the years that were worse than wasted dropping from him, and the vigour of early manhood with its hopes and ambitions returning.'

With testimonials like this Keeley's fame spread like wildfire. Soon Dwight had become the 'Parent House' and forty or fifty branch institutes sprang up in Texas, Iowa, Philadelphia, Ohio, Kansas, California, Utah, anywhere where there were people whose thirsts had got the better of them. Naturally Keeley prospered and when he died at the turn of the century he was a millionaire.

What sort of a man was this Dr Keeley who left his laboratory one evening convinced that he had the cure of drunkenness within his grasp? Someone who knew him well wrote to the *Chicago Tribune* thus: 'Instantly upon meeting Dr Keeley, a student of character feels that he is in the presence of a great man, nor does this impression grow less with acquaintance. On the contrary, the first conception is strengthened. I have seen great generals and have interviewed statesmen, and have come away feeling that the public have overrated them: but the more I contemplate Dr Keeley the more I am convinced that he is a really great man – a great scientist. He is surely doing more good than any man living today: more good than any statesman or any philanthropist.'

The writer was a journalist and if it were a genuinely expressed opinion it should carry great weight. Some other people were not quite so enthusiastic about the good doctor and his institute. In London in the 1890's there was a Society for the Study of Inebriety. Regular meetings were held and various papers were read and discussed. One such paper was presented by a Dr Usher from Melbourne, Australia. He described a visit made to Dwight to study, rather than partake of, the Cure. Dr Keeley appeared unimpressive to this visitor. When Dr Usher asked questions as to exactly what the treatment was, he seemed uneasy, and replied, 'We will not go into that. I know it's all right. If you want to learn about it, the secretary-chemist will tell you.' Unfortunately the secretary-chemist turned out to be a sort of glorified office boy. Dr Usher was introduced to Keeley's 'Chief of Staff,' a Dr Blair, and the rest of the medical staff. His comment on these gentlemen was as terse as it was economical. They were 'unsuccessful practitioners,' he said. Perhaps these two words meant a lot.

And yet while he was at the institute Dr Usher seems to have found out quite a lot about the bichloride of gold cure. The injections that patients received regularly were simply atropine. In large doses (and there is evidence that Dr Keeley used large doses as his patients often complained of blurring of vision and partial blindness after the injection), atropine is a stimulant of the central nervous system causing restlessness, talkativeness and hallucinations. Other effects of atropine are dryness of the mouth, inhibition of intestinal motility and inhibition of glandular secretions. It is difficult to see how it could have had any effect beneficially or otherwise on an alcoholic. Was the secret of the treatment in the medicine, then? Some of this was obtained and analysed. The result was water 61 per cent, sugar 6 per cent, alcohol 25 per cent and lime salts to 100 per cent. Gold, either as a chloride or in any other form was conspicuous by its absence. What the sufferers were getting for their medicine was a drink about the potency of sherry.

It is no wonder that Dr Keeley could say truthfully, 'The sobering up process of Dwight is a small matter – I take him from inebriety to sobriety much as a ship is lifted from the water to a dry dock, without strain.' Two-hourly doses of the cure and as much whisky as they required in the early stages would certainly make this possible. Many alcoholics would consider their 25 dollars a week 'remedy and treatment charge,' well spent. Often when they 'graduated' from Dwight they carried on with treatment at home at 4½ dollars a bottle.

Alive to every business opportunity, Dr Keeley made an attempt to float a syndicate in England. The idea was to raise £150,000 to purchase the rights of using the gold cure so that the inhabitants of these islands could benefit in the same way as their American brothers. Unhappily for Dr Keeley the activities of the Society for the study of Inebriety and adverse publicity prevented the golden grog from flowing.

Amazing as it may seem the Keeley Institute is still going strong, but it is under 'entirely new management.' Now staffed by two doctors, one of which is a psychiatrist, orthodox medical treatment of inebriation is carried out. Prices are high judged by British standards (110 dollars a week minimum). But quackery has gone out of the cure. Dwight has grown up for in 1954 the village celebrated its centenary. A United States senator writing about Dwight in that year stated that 'Dwight has preserved an unhurried tranquillity and sweetness in periods of strifes and tension.' He recalled Goldsmith's lines when referring to the 'loveliest village of the plain where health and plenty cheered the labouring swain.'

The old institute buildings have been converted into a veterans' hospital and the impressive new institute is situated in about '20 acres of well landscaped park grounds with deer paddocks, artificial lake, etc., for the interest and amusement of the patients.'

Is there anything at all to be said for the activities of the old Keeley Institute or was the whole thing 100 per cent bogus? In all fairness it must be admitted that several of the principles of the gold cure still hold good in most modern treatments of the alcoholic. One or two newer drugs such as Antabuse, have admittedly been introduced into the therapeutic armamentarium of doctors dealing with these problems, but on the whole, things have not changed much in sixty-odd years. The most effective way of dealing with alcoholics is to remove them from the environment in which their alcoholism developed. Then gradually wean them off their alcoholic beverages, usually on to some other 'tranquilliser.' Finally, after they have got over these early struggles it has been found effective to introduce them to other people who have been through the same process. This practical form of group psychotherapy is the basis of the Alcoholics Anonymous clubs that exist almost everywhere today.

If Dr Keeley had stuck to these ideas as the basis of his treatment, and not concentrated on the fictitious bichloride of gold, he may well have gone down in the Annals of Medicine as a benefactor of mankind instead of a barely remembered, thinly disguised quack doctor who made a million.

6

JAMES GRAHAM – MASTERQUACK

Medical Institutes did not ever become popular in England. A few like 'Dr Hunter's Institute of Anatomy,' in Great Charles Street, Birmingham, flourished for a while, but adverse publicity soon closed them down. But once upon a time, towards the end of the 18th century to be more precise, there was a prosperous medical institute in London. Its owner, Dr James Graham, would not have approved of the comparison at all. Perhaps it is not fair to compare them for the American model worked with fear as its driving force. The English one relied on mankind's interest in Health, Beauty and Sex. Another discrepancy between the 20th-century American Institutes and their 18th-century British counterpart, is that the American centres were usually sited in poor neighbourhoods. James Graham's Temples of Health were exclusively situated in smart surroundings.

Dr James Graham, 'M.D.', is probably the most interesting figure in Quackery of all time. His career makes fascinating reading. He was born in 1745 in the Cowgate district of Edinburgh, which was, judging by contemporary prints, not a particularly salubrious neighbourhood. His father was a saddler. He must have been a pretty successful one for by the time his children, three daughters and two sons, had grown up, he was in a position to educate them and launch them on a modest scale in Edinburgh society. One of the three daughters contracted a good marriage with the 'Celebrated Dr Arnold of Leicester,' Fellow of the Royal College of Physicians. The other two girls married local men of no great distinction. The two boys, James and William, studied medicine at Edinburgh University. William, the younger brother, qualified and practised some

112

time as a physician before abandoning his medical career for the
Church. He eventually entered into holy orders.

Whether James qualified in medicine or not is rather a moot
point. We are informed that after having finished his studies at
Edinburgh he went to England and began in business in
Pontefract where he married and raised a family. Whatever the
business was it did not absorb James for long, for the next we
hear of him he is in America. New England contained, apparently,
a large number of patients suffering from the 'most desperate
diseases.' These were cases that had hitherto puzzled the
ordinary practitioners. This was right up Dr Graham's street
for he, 'having the advantage of a good person, polite address,
and agreeable conversation,' introduced himself into the 'first
circles, where he made a lot of money.' Here we find one of the
interesting incongruities in James Graham's life. Of all places
for a young English 'Physician' to pick, America would seem to
have been the worst. The American War of Independence
(1775) would surely have made Englishmen rather unpopular,
even around Philadelphia where Graham lived and practised.
And yet he was there in the 1770's doing quite well. He was
back in Europe in 1779 when he is reported to have been in
practice in Paris for a short time. There he won the approval,
medically speaking, of Georgiana, the famous Duchess of Devon-
shire. Just before his first venture in London he is reported as
being 'so popular' among his patients in Edinburgh that he
might have settled in the city in a fashionable practice, to 'great
advantage.'

What was the secret of Graham's success in these early days?
Firstly comes his personality and appearance. The fascination of
his manner is frequently mentioned by his contemporaries. His
appearance was said to be such that 'when walking with him all
the women turned round to look at him.' Appearance alone does
not do much for a doctor. The real secret of Graham's early
success must have been in his methods of treatment and his
professional reputation. Exactly what Graham did in these early
days is not really known. But in 1777 he was carrying out what
might be described as electrical treatments on people of rank
and quality. One of his famous patients was Katherine Macaulay,
who eventually became his sister-in-law. The technique of
Graham's treatment at this time was quite simple. He merely

placed his patients on a 'magnetic throne,' or in a bath and gave them mild electric shocks. Other more conventional treatments included milk baths and 'frictions.'

Graham has been said to have come under the influence of Benjamin Franklin. It has been suggested that the great experimental scientist was responsible in some way for Graham's foibles. This could hardly be the case for when Franklin was publishing his papers on electricity Graham was only a boy of eight. There is little doubt, however, that Graham did meet Franklin in America and again in Paris in 1779. At this time Franklin was deeply involved in politics and was American Foreign Minister to France. It is doubtful whether the great man would have had much time for a peripatetic Quack doctor, particularly if he felt that the scientific aspects of electricity were being exploited.

In the 1780's the medical uses of electricity were just being realised. Before me as I write is an essay on the theory and practice of medical electricity, by Tiberius Cavallo, Fellow of the Royal Society, printed in 1781. This one hundred and twenty-four page book gives a good contemporary account of the subject from a scientific viewpoint. It describes the machines that were used to 'shock' the patients in great detail. The principle of the treatment was simple. A high electro-static charge was transmitted on to a 'prime conductor' probably by a friction machine. Wires and leads were taken from this in such a way that graduated shocks could be transmitted to a patient by various electrodes. After giving the 'theory of medical electricity and directions for the practical application' of the same, the book goes on to quote 'general rules of practice' and 'authentic cases in which electricity was administered.' Ten cases are mentioned, three of which were reported in the Philosophical Transactions of the Royal Society, in which electricity was used to good effect.

The modern medical reader would soon detect that these cases were self limiting diseases that would have recovered spontaneously anyway, or hysterical phenomena which would be very susceptible to the suggestion of a cure – especially a cure so electrically dramatic. James Graham's active mind realised the potentialities of this new magic. He may even have been impressed by them himself. The expression half knave-half fool has been used referring to Graham, but on due consideration there was little of the fool in the doctor's judgement as far as the possibilities of electricity, quackwise, were concerned.

If Graham had rested on his laurels as a successful travelling Quack, he would have gained himself a permanent but unimpressive place in the History of Quackery. But life for James Graham really began at the age of thirty-five when he opened the Temple of Health in the year 1780. This raised him above all others in the hierarchy of his profession. Characteristically he obtained an elegant Adams-designed house in the centre of Adelphi Terrace for his operations. To mark it well and make it easily distinguished (street numbering had not yet become general), he had an enormous golden star fixed on the front of the house and the words Templum Aesculapio Sacrum emblazoned over the entrance.

Henry Angelo, court fencing master to George IV gives us in his *Reminiscences*, an eye witness account of people arriving at the Temple for an evening performance. 'I remember,' he writes, 'the carriages drawing up next to the door of this modern Paphos, with crowds of gaping sparks on either side, to discover who were the visitors, but the ladies' faces were covered, all going incognito. At the door stood two gigantic porters, with each a long staff, with ornamental silver head, like those borne by parish beadles, and wearing superb liveries, with large, gold-laced cocked hats, each was near seven feet in height, and retained to keep the entrance clear.'

The pavement outside the Temple was incredibly narrow and one step took the visitor from his coach into the impressive hall. Here guests were relieved of their two-guinea entrance fee and got their first impressions of the interior. Every room inside was set out on the most lavish scale. The walls were hung with long draped mirrors. The furnishings were described by Angelo, who lived in the environment of Royal palaces and grand houses, as 'magnificent.' In one such room Dr Graham gave his celebrated lectures of which more will be said later. To illustrate his lectures he used a series of beautiful girls who were referred to as Goddesses of Health.

These young women, chosen for their physical beauty and charm, posed in various degrees of undress to show what could be expected in the way of physical perfection if one followed the Graham method. Their identity was anonymous, they being referred to by the doctor, as 'Hebe Vestina,' or the 'Goddess of Youth and Health.' There is one possible exception to this rule, a girl who was to become known later as Lady Hamilton. Emma Lyons, as she was then, was certainly in London at about the right time, being in 1780 employed as a nursemaid in the house of a Dr Budd. She was then sixteen. Young people in their teens, particularly those of Emma's temperament, often change their jobs frequently. During the next two years she was working as a domestic to a tradesman in the West End of London, i.e. the vicinity of the Temple of Health and later as a lady's companion where, incidentally, she took part in family theatrical entertainments showing 'great talent.'

Emma had, to quote from a contemporary's description, 'a perfect figure, fine regular features, and an indescribable charm and attractiveness about her face and expression.' In other words she would have been a natural for Dr Graham's exhibition which was closely approximating at times to what we might now call a Skin Show. That Emma was not a particularly modest or retiring young lady is shown by the fact that shortly after her employment as a lady's maid she was living as mistress to a Naval Captain (Captain, later Admiral Payne). Again during the same year she was similarly connected with Sir Harry Featherstonehaugh. In between these affairs she might well have signed on for employment with Graham, particularly as we know that at this time she had frequent periods of penury. Nevertheless most of Lady Hamilton's biographers stoutly deny the assertion, none more strongly than Angelo himself.

He had something of a liaison with her, his account of which is interesting. 'Returning from my professional pursuits, at the corner of New Compton Street, my feelings were excited by the figure of a young woman, meanly attired, in the attitude of dejection, leaning against the post. Pausing some time, I could not resist speaking to her, and said, "My poor girl, you seem to be very unhappy, can I be of a service to you." Several times did I address her without effect, nor would she even look at me: I was disconcerted and with some zeal (at the moment seeing an acquaintance coming towards me), said, "Will you be here tonight at eight?" With a deep drawn sigh, she replied: "Yes."

I was punctual so was she.' Angelo obviously took her off somewhere and later asked her about herself. She was apparently reticent about her past but confided that 'she had not tasted food that day.' Angelo was not ready to spend a lot of money on a casual pick-up as he economically 'ordered some biscuits to be placed before her,' which 'she devoured in a voracious manner.' The fair maiden told him, however, that her name was Emma, but little else, and arranged to meet him the next night.

Angelo thought better of it and did not keep the assignation. He saw her a few days later accompanied by two 'elegants' in Kensington Gardens, no longer in 'mean attire' but in all 'grandeur of fashion.' His conclusion that she was not the Goddess of Health rests on two points. Firstly, he had seen at the Temple the 'female who was lectured upon, who had no more clothing than Venus when she rose from the sea.' She was not Emma Lyons he said. Secondly, he had followed Emma's career after his night out with her — and she had not appeared at Dr Graham's temple since then, anyway. This does not preclude her appearing at the temple before meeting Angelo, of course. There was more than one Goddess of Health. In all probability there were several. When Graham wanted a fresh 'Hebe Vestina' he advertised: 'Wanted genteel, decent, modest young woman; she must be personally agreeable, blooming, healthy, and sweet tempered and well recommended for modesty, good sense and steadiness. She is to live in the Physician's family, to be daily dressed in white silk robes with a rich rose coloured girdle. If she can sing, play on the harpsichord or speak French greater wages will be given. Enquire Dr Graham, Adelphi Temple.'

It was not only the viewing of the fair Emma's, or anyone else's physical charms, that brought Graham fame and drew the crowds.

The main draw was the Celestial Bed. This magnificent apparatus was in a separate room that had a private entrance from the street. This was probably just as well considering the purposes for which the bed was designed. The best description of the bed is Graham's own. Here it is:

The Grand Celestial Bed, whose magical influences are now celebrated from pole to pole and from the rising to the setting of the sun, is 12 ft. long by 9 ft. wide, supported by forty pillars of brilliant glass of the most exquisite workmanship, in richly varigated colours. The super-celestial dome of the bed, which contains the odoriferous, balmy and ethereal spices, odours and essences, which is the grand reservoir of those reviving invigorating influences which are exhaled by the breath of the music and by the exhilarating force of electrical fire, is covered on the other side with brilliant panes of looking-glass.

On the utmost summit of the dome are placed two exquisite figures of Cupid and Psyche, with a figure of Hymen behind, with his torch flaming with electrical fire in one hand and with the other, supporting a celestial crown, sparkling over a pair of living turtle doves, on a little bed of roses.

The other elegant group of figures which sport on the top of the dome, having each of them musical instruments in their hands, which by the most expensive mechanism, breathe forth sound corresponding to their instruments, flutes, guitars, violins, clarinets, trumpets, horns, oboes, kettle drums, etc.

The post or pillars too, which support the grand dome are groups of musical instruments, golden pipes, etc., which in sweet concert breathe forth celestial sounds, lulling the visions of Elysian joys.

At the head of the bed appears sparkling with electrical fire a great first commandment: 'BE FRUITFUL, MULTIPLY AND REPLENISH THE EARTH.' Under that is an elegant sweet-toned organ in front of which is a fine landscape of moving figures, priest and bride's procession entering the Temple of Hymen.

In the Celestial Bed no feather bed is employed but sometimes mattresses filled with sweet new wheat or oat straw mingled with balm, rose leaves, lavender flowers and oriental spices. The sheets are of the richest and softest silk, stained of various colours suited to the complexion. Pale green, rose colour, sky blue, white and purple, and are sweetly perfumed in oriental manner with the tudor rose, or with rich gums or balsams.

The chief principle of my Celestial Bed is produced by artificial lodestones. About 15 cwt. of compound magnets are continually pouring forth in an everflowing circle.

The bed is constructed with a double frame, which moves on an axis or pivot and can be converted into an inclined plane.

Sometimes the mattresses are filled with the strongest, most springy hair, produced at vast expense from the tails of English stallions which are elastic to the highest degree.

Even allowing for the inventor's natural enthusiasm the Celestial Bed must have been pretty impressive. It was said to have cost Graham some £10,000 and had been made by an expert tinsmith called Denton. Graham is quite dogmatic about what the bed was for. In one of his lectures he states:

Should pregnancy at any time not happily ensue I have the most astonishing method to recommend which will infallibly produce a genial and happy issue, I mean my Celestial or Magnetico-electrico bed, which is the first and only ever in the world: it is placed in a spacious room to the right of my orchestra which produces the Celestial fire and the vivifying influence: this brilliant Celestial Bed is supported by six massive brass pillars with Saxon blue and purple satin, perfumed with Arabian spices in the style of those in the Seraglio of a Grand Turk. Any gentleman and his lady desirous of progeny, and wishing to spend an evening in the Celestial apartment, after coition may, by a complement of a £50 bank note be permitted to partake of the heavenly joys it affords by causing immediate conception, accompanied by the soft music. Superior ecstasy which the parties enjoy in the Celestial Bed is really astonishing and never before thought of in this world: the barren must certainly become fruitful when they are powerfully agitated in the delights of love.

The tilting mechanism of the bed deserves mention. Many reputable doctors during Graham's day, when the scientific facts regarding fertility were only half known, advocated that a woman should lie still for a considerable period after coitus. This was obviously believed to facilitate impregnation of the ovum by the spermatozoa. There is probably a lot of practical good sense in this idea for certain primitive tribes practise a successful form of contraception that involves sudden athletic movement by the woman after coitus. Graham's tilting bed would tend to further facilitate impregnation of its female occupants. Thus we see Graham applying a little practical science to his quackery.

The stallion's hair that he refers to is a different matter entirely. This is a case of 'influence by association.' Stallions are well known to be virile and fertile. The implication is that coitus occurring on a bed of stallions' tails would be blessed in the same way.

The cost of a night in the Celestial Bed seems to have varied. Graham himself mentions £50. Angelo states that 'many a nobleman paid Graham £500 to draw the curtains.' Unfortunately, there is no record of anybody expressing an opinion of the value of a night in the Celestial Bed, but its fame obviously passed by word of mouth. Many notable personalities visited the Temple of Health. They were not all as impressed as Angelo. Horace Walpole was not amused. He referred to it as 'the most impudent puppet show of imposition' he ever saw. Southey was also unimpressed. Nevertheless, the Temple flourished.

In 1781 Graham decided that a move was necessary, but just why nobody knows. His biographer in the *Dictionary of National Biography* states that the expenses of the Adelphi establishment forced him to move to Shomberg House, Pall Mall. Others imply that the Adelphi Temple was so successful that it was too small to hold the numbers seeking admission. Walpole's evidence is against the latter being true (there were only eighteen present when he heard Graham give his lecture). Graham's own advertisements of the time always asked people to arrive in good time to ensure that the ladies present could obtain seats. This may well have been a publicity splurge. One explanation for the move has not been put forward and yet there is evidence in a contemporary manuscript that Graham had to cope in the 18th century with a 20th-century problem – neighbour trouble!

Frederick Reynolds, who published his *Life and Times* in 1826, lived just behind the Temple. He and his friends found the good doctor's establishment a great source of amusement. To quote from his book 'daily, he (Graham) attracted overflowing audiences, and the back of his house being opposite to the back of ours, we occasionally took a view of his performance, gratis. This was a cause of sore discontent to the doctor, and many a rebuke for us. But, as a much more heavy cause of complaint against us, was our martial habit of discharging from our first-floor window, with all the force of fingers, thumbs and arms, paper pellets full against the eager visages of the doctor's patients. This excited the enemy's anger to such a degree that one evening, we received an anonymous letter, evidently written by him, stating that "he and his spectators were compelled, to the positive detriment of their systems, to close the windows on the hottest days, lest a paper pellet with a pin in its end be conveyed to the eye. Beware, or you shall hear more from a terrace observer." '

To this Reynolds replied in verse.

'Dear Doctor,
'Tis not true that our pellets are charged with a pin,

A Mesmeric crisis. Some of the 'bribes' that Mesmer offered
his patients are well illustrated here

Cruikshank's comment on Mr Morison, the Hygeist

An early 19th
Century Quack
cartoon

*Wellcome Historical
Medical Library*

A 'genuine' Quack
diploma

*American Medical
Association*

But supposing they are, pray where is the sin?
Grant we put out your eye, well you'll put it in.'

This rather amusing incident shows that even in his heyday Graham was not universally popular. There may have been others who disapproved of his practice on their doorsteps, lowering the tone of the neighbourhood. We are indebted to Reynolds also for positive evidence that there was more than one Goddess of Health. He related that one of his particular friends had formed 'a most marked predilection for the doctor's principle performer.' Luckily or unluckily, however, just as the lover's flame was growing into a conflagration, the Goddess of Health fell sick and died: owing, wags said, 'to a cold given by the damp sheets of the Celestial Bed!'

Spring 1781 saw the opening of the new establishment, called the Temple of Health and Hymen, in Shomberg House, Pall Mall. Pall Mall during the 18th century was quite an exciting place. It was then, as now, the home of many clubs, coffee houses and inns. In one of the latter, the Star and Garter, the fatal duel between Lord Byron and Mr Chatsworth was fought. Strangers to the town often made Pall Mall their temporary residence due to its central position. It was also a centre for shows and exhibitions, curiosities being displayed on 'public raffing days.'

George Psalmanazar lived in Pall Mall. There he 'passed for an islander of Formosa and invented a language that baffled the best philologists in Europe.' Another resident celebrity belonged to a now long forgotten type, curious to the 18th century. He was Joseph Clark, the Posture master. His speciality was impersonating deformities, many of which, it was claimed, 'baffled surgeons and perplexed the tailor's measure.' It is curious that such a performance could be classed as entertainment. Other parts of Pall Mall were famous for entertainments of a less respectable nature. King's Place, Pall Mall, was noted as an area for brothels.

It was here that the celebrated Mrs Hayes provided her patrons with the very best that could be expected in 18th-century debauchery. In a Serail that catered largely for the aristocracy she had many Lords and Ladies as regular customers. Mrs Hayes provided not only what might be expected from a fashionable 18th-century brothel but also staged elaborate indecent entertainments. In one of these 'twelve beautiful nymphs, spotless virgins, would carry out the famous feast of Venus, as it is celebrated in Tahiti.' The nymphs were joined in what is usually accepted as a strictly private act by 'twelve athletic youths.' It is reported that twenty-three visitors of a high standing, including five members of the House of Commons, attended.

Another incredible entertainment was the 'Bal d'Amour,' staged by brothel-keeper Mrs Prendergast. Admission was 5 gns. for this debauch at which the dancers wore only fig-leaves. Mrs Prendergast 'provided a good band of music, who were so disposed as to afford their harmonious assistance without being admitted spectators on the festive scene.' An elegant cold collation was also prepared with wines of all kinds in abundance. On this Gala night Pall Mall was thronged with chairs and carriages. After the 'guests' had danced for a couple of hours, the cold collation was served and toasts were drunk to the 'Cyprian Goddess and her Rites.'

After this 'the scene changed and presented a camera obscura, with a proper number of sofas, to realise those rites which had been celebrated (previously) only in theory.' A full description of this lascivious scene, given in the *History of King's Place*, contains thinly disguised references to various members of the peerage and other London socialites who were present. Mrs Prendergast, it is estimated, made some £1,000 out of this particular evening's 'entertainment.'

Shomberg House itself was built during Cromwell's time. It was one of half a dozen houses on the south side of Pall Mall, surrounded by fields and meadows that stretched out behind them towards the Royal Gardens, now the private grounds of Marlborough House. During Charles II's day Nell Gwynne lived next door. Later in the reign of William III the house was repaired and beautified by Frederick, Duke of Shomberg, who gave the house its name. During the 18th century it became the home of many painters. Astley, Cosway, and later Gainsborough, used parts of the house as residences and studios. It would appear that even in these days large houses were split up into flats, for Gainsborough paid £300 per year for the West Wing.

When the new Temple of Health opened it was with a blaze of publicity. Handbills and newspapers gave the glad tidings to the awaiting populace. Grose, the 18th-century antiquarian and literary Falstaff, includes several Graham handbills in his intriguing book *The Guide to Health*, that was published in 1773.

This collection of advertisements and handbills gives great insight into the foibles of the 18th century. For instance, we find the interesting dual occupation of Dentist-Dancing Master advertised. He could provide a set of false teeth for 10 guineas and a box of toothpaste for 2/6. The price of the dancing lessons is not mentioned. A marriage market surely not inferior to the modern *Matrimonial Post* was obviously popular and necessary. ('A gentleman of fortune, whom family reasons oblige to drop a connection which has for some time subsisted between him and an agreeable young lady, will give a considerable sum of money, with her, to any gentleman, etc., etc.') Stock exchange tips were given alongside advertisements for water closets and breeches makers (improved by geometry!). Mr Maxfield, 'his late Majesty's coach painter, 'solicited' favour in every branch of the painting business, from a hovel to a palace, and from a whisky to a state coach.' An advertiser announcing that he had vacancies for providing 'lunatics with board and lodging,' vied with conjurers, fire eaters, chimney sweeps and 'curious exhibitions,' for the reader's attention.

A prominent handbill addressed with customary Graham thoroughness to 'Their Excellencies, the Foreign Ambassadors, the Nobility, Gentry and persons of learning and taste' announced that 'This and tomorrow evening the Celestial brilliancy of the Medico-Electrical apparatus at the Temple will be exhibited by Dr Graham himself. Previous to the display the Doctor will delicately touch upon the celestial beds, which are soon to be opened in the Temple of Health, Pall Mall, for the propagating of beings rational, and far stronger and more beautiful in mental as well as bodily endowment, than the present puny, feeble and nonsensical race of probationary mortals, which crawl, fret and politely play at cutting one another's throats for nothing at all, on most parts of this terraqueous globe.' Admission was 5/– at night or 2/6 during the day. A later handbill gave evidence of the success of the lecture for it stated that 'there have been these last evenings past an overflow of at least nine hundred ladies and gentlemen. It will be continued this and every evening this week in chaste and joyous assemblage!'

Graham reported also that there were between 800 and 1,600 ladies and gentlemen in the 'great Apollo chamber at the lecture and walking about in the open apartments of this celestial paradise.' An advertisement in the *Morning Post* also heralded the opening of the new Temple. It stated that 'The Temple of Health, Pall Mall, will be open this and every evening this week, as a grand Elysian promenade, which will now, for the first time, be conducted by Dr Graham himself, with that decency and decorum, with that ease and eloquence, with that peace and propriety, which he flatters himself will ensure the satisfaction and happiness of the nobility and gentry of both sexes who honour him with their presence, and the approbation and protection of all upright and disinterested magistrates. *N.B.* – The rooms will be superbly illuminated with virgin wax, aromatic odour, and harmonious sounds will be breathed forth from the altar of the great electrical temple; and the whole electrical apparatus which is infinitely larger and more magnificent than any other that ever was erected in the world, will be displayed in all the celestial brilliancy of that universal, most resplendent and tremendous fire.'

Although at Pall Mall prices were generally lower, the Temple of Hymen was attracting more attention than the Adelphi establishment ever did. Samuel Curwin, writing his *Journal* on the 19th February, 1783, gives his impression of an evening spent at the Temple:

Evening at Dr James's lecture on health in his Temple of Health in Pall Mall, near St James. The first room entered was properly the vestibule, from whence, through folding doors, one passes into the apartment holding the Electric Bed. Passing this you enter the room of Apollo, through a narrow entry, having on each hand two or three niches containing statues, gilded, about half the natural size. The first object that meets the eye is the Temple of Apollo, being a round cupola five feet in diameter, supported by six fluted pillars of the Corinthian order, and eight feet high, in imitation of Scagliola. In the centre stands a Tripodal Frame with concave sides on which rests in each angle a lion couchant, supporting a long frame of the branch of six or eight lamps, adorned or rather over charged with crystals, whose tremulous action, by the company's walking, adds great brilliancy to the appearance, the walls all around having many branches with three candles each, besides two more large central branches, suspended by gilt chains, from the ceiling. Decorations in the frippery kind are in great profusion in this as well as in the other room, consisting of glass in various forms and sizes, inlaid and hanging:

many gilt statues of Apollo, Venus, Hercules, Aesculapius, besides a few pictures. The master discovered a great elocution, a great medical knowledge, and appeared well qualified to support the character he assumes.

The German Army officer, W. D. Archenholtz, in his *Picture of England*, also described the Temple. He asserted that Graham had:

A perfect knowledge of the human heart, the success which attended his experiment proves that he has calculated with judgement. He has too much sense to be suspected of being a dupe to the occult science which he professed and must therefore be classed in the list of cunning and politic adventurers . . . Nothing indeed is more superb than his Temple. Electrical fire, managed with judgement ascended in radiating streams: transparent glasses of every different colour chosen and placed with taste, rich vases filled with the purest perfumes, which gently awaken desire, filled the soul with a sof ' nguor . . . The more that this holy of holies began to be visited, th ore did this sagacious high priest add to the voluptuous magnifice... of the place!

The French, too, were hearing about the miracles of Pall Mall. The following quotation from an anonymous first-hand observer writing the *Correspondance Secrète*, adds a little more to our mental picture of the Temple:

The façade is ornamented with three figures, those of Venus, having on one side Minerva and on the other Juno. Underneath are the following inscriptions, 'Temple of Health, The happiness of Monarchs, The Riches of the Poor.' Lower down is seen a statue dedicated to Aesculapius. Lastly there is a legend on the door to the following effect: 'No guard watches at this gate, so that entrance may be free to the rich as to the poor.' In spite of this inscription, two men of lofty stature clad in flowing robes wearing a cuirasse on which is written Temple of Health, allow no one to enter until an entrance fee is paid.

Scarcely has one set foot on the first step on the staircase than one hears harmonious strains of wind instruments which reach the ear through hidden openings in the staircase, while the sweetest perfumes flatter the sense of smell till the entrance of a magnificent apartment is reached. This is used for the delivery of lectures, in which the Doctor professes to abolish barrenness, although he himself has never had any children. [An obvious error.] He uses the plainest language in dealing with the parts concerned in generation; yet ladies as well as men crowd to hear him without a scruple.

Garlands, mirrors, crystals, gilt and silver ornaments are scattered about with profusion so that from all parts they reflect a dazzling light. Music precedes each lecture from five o'clock till seven when Dr Graham presents himself, vested in doctor's robes. On the instant there follows a silence which is interrupted only at the end of the lecture by an electric shock, given to the whole audience by means of conductors hidden under the cushions with which all the seats are covered. While some jest at the astonishment of the others a spirit is seen to emerge from under the floor of the room: it presents the appearance of a man of gigantic stature, thin and haggard, who without uttering a word, hands the doctor a bottle of liquor which, after having been shown to the company, is carried off by the spirit.

To this strange apparition succeeds a pretty woman under the form of the Goddess of Music, who after singing six pieces vanishes in her turn. Dr Graham having finished his lecture, the audience breaks up without daring to express regret for the money expended on so extraordinary a spectacle. Before the sittings the Doctor makes a public offer to dissipate the melancholy and mitigate extravagant gaiety. All these details, however, are only accessories of his establishment. The sumptuous bed in brocaded damasks is supported by four crystal pillars of spiral shape. On whatever side one gets into this bed, which is called Celestial, one hears an organ played in unison with three others which make agreeable music consisting of varied airs which carry the happy couples into the arms of Morpheus. For nearly an hour that the concert lasts one sees in the bed streams of light which play especially over the pillars. When the time for getting up has come, the magician comes to feel the pulse of the faithful, gives them breakfast, and sends them away full of hope, not forgetting to recommend them to send him other clients.

The exploitation of sex, and the magical allurement of electricity were important cards in Graham's hands, but his lectures were obviously trumps. Most of Graham's biographers dismiss the famous lectures as 'tissues of obscenities,' or 'infamous writings.' A closer analysis of these lectures reveals that they were neither obscene nor infamous. Admittedly Graham got rather near the bone towards the middle of his lecture on generation. While addressing himself to those 'in whose veins the Venus creeps or loiters,' he advocates that they 'at certain critical and important times' should have 'their passions roused and excited, by the sight of rich warm, or what are called lascivious prints, statues and paintings.' Likewise, when conception had not taken place 'in the ordinary course of things' he recommends 'celebrating the rites of Venus in a variety of ways and places . . . for some women have actually been got with child in one attitude who never could be impregnated in any other.'

While he was expounding on this subject he explains how the first idea of the Celestial Bed came into his mind. When he was in Philadelphia he 'speedily insulated a common bedstead and filled it with copious streams of electrical fire conveyed by metal rods enclosed in glass tubes through the partition, from the adjacent room where the great globes were wrought . . . I recommended the trial of this, then whimsical bed, to several of my medical, philosophical and gay friends . . .' Later he states that after he had put them at ease by means of a few drinks he went so far as to ask them for their opinion of the bed. Delightedly he states that 'they talked not as other men might have done of the critical moment – no, they talked comparatively of the critical hour.'

Graham's audience obviously wanted information on aphrodisiacs. He was dead against the popular Spanish Fly preparations. Cantharides poisoning obviously occurred in the 18th as well as in the 20th century. Graham's advice on the subject was to the point if rather crude. Modern psychiatrists, including Dr Kinsey, talk of voyeurism. This term merely means that sexual stimulation can occur quite frequently as a result of visual stimulation. Graham recounts the tale of how a hairdresser, who found himself impotent was suddenly filled with sexual desire while he was dressing a particularly lovely woman's hair. Imprudently, he downed tools and ran home to make his wife happy. Such was the power of voyeurism in this case. Another Graham anecdote on this subject is about an old debauched woman who still desired masculine attention but who could not arouse a lover's interest. Her cure, he says, was to take a lovely young woman to bed with her. If her lover's ardour flagged the presence of his mistress's companion was sufficient to restore the *status quo*. This is about as far as Graham goes with regard to obscenity. A great many of his contemporaries would have left him standing.

For the most part the lectures were good sound stuff. For instance, he was keen on washing the body frequently. This was not a particularly popular habit in the 18th century. Graham states, rather poetically, that it is necessary to 'tune body and

mind for the most cordial and perfect enjoyment of prolific love.'
To do this he said it was necessary that the lovers should possess
'the sweetest, freshest, and most personal cleanliness from the
top of the head, to the end of the most distant toe – at all times
and under every circumstance.' Graham was also very much
against double beds. He stated that there was 'nothing more
unnatural, nothing more indecent, than man and wife continually
pigging together in one and the same bed . . . and to sleep and
snore and steam and do everything else indelicate together 365
times every year!' Sleeping in double beds was, according to
Graham, a state of 'matrimonial whoredom.'

He was also a great advocate of fresh air, which must have
been pretty startling at the time. Sea voyages, an active and
useful life, taking exercise daily in free open air, were all recommended as adjuncts to good health. His attitude towards alcohol
was dogmatic. Particularly he refers to 'that poisonous composition of sloes, tartar, logwood, watery cider and brandy which is
called port wine.' Graham realised, nearly two hundred years
ago, that alcohol diminished physical, and more important to
his audience, perhaps, sexual performance.

Some of Graham's ideas seemed to sow the seeds of Vic-
torianism as far as sex was concerned. Masturbation and
fornication he abhorred. 'I must speak plainly, gentlemen, every
act of self-pollution, every repetition of natural venery, with
even the loveliest of the sex, to which appalled and exhausted
nature is whipped and spurred by lust . . . is an earthquake, a
blast, a deadly paralytic stroke to all the faculties of both soul
and body. Blasting beauty, chilling, contracting and enfeebling
the body, mind and the memory!' And yet in other ways he was
right up-to-date. Writing on the encouragement of matrimony
he advocated that the first step would be to 'suppress all public
prostitution,' as it 'destroys the vigour of the genital parts,
necessity tempting them to too frequent acts of venery.' Some
180 years later, an Act of Parliament finally drove the majority
of prostitutes off the streets of Britain.

Another of Graham's ideas for encouraging matrimony was
to 'give certain rewards to the lower and middling class of
people, and tax those proportionate to their circumstances who
did not marry.' He also advised that parents should 'receive a
small premium on the birth of every child.' He thus foresaw

Graham and Katterfelto

Dr Graham with a few 'patients' at the earthbaths in Panton Street

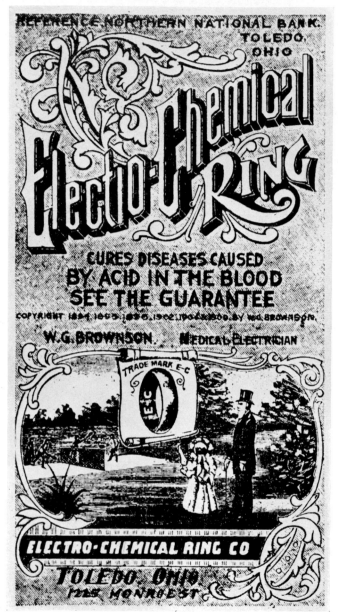

American Medical Association

modern income tax laws and the National Insurance and the Social Security system operating in this country. He advocated the control of certain hereditary diseases by practical eugenics. 'Persons of certain descriptions, whose constitutions are infected with inherent diseases, ought not to marry . . . they ought to be tied back to old women . . . that are past child-bearing.' Public opinion in this country has never really supported ideas along these lines, but 28 States in America have laws that permit or direct sterilisation for various causes. Since these laws have been enforced, over 27,000 people have been sterilised in the United States.

The year 1783 was the turning point in Graham's career. Until that time everything he touched had gone right. But now it was obvious that the Pall Mall establishment was losing money. Graham attempted to increase his profits by lowering prices, always a dangerous practice, especially for a Quack. Eventually creditors pressed and the Temple was closed, its treasures, electrical machines and even the Celestial Bed being sold up to pay bad debts. Graham returned to his native land and was soon in trouble with the magistrates of Edinburgh for giving a lecture 'deemed improper for public discussions.' Apparently Scottish public opinion was not as broadminded as its English counterpart for Graham repeatedly fell foul of the law and was even imprisoned in the Tollbooth for 'his late injurious publications in this City.'

During the years 1784 and 1785, Graham may have had some ideas of becoming a regular physician for he attended lectures in Chemistry, Anatomy, the practice and theory of Medicine and Materia Medica at Edinburgh University. He never qualified, however. A little later he showed signs that his former eccentricities were leading him along a path that was to end in insanity. In 1788 he was sent off from Whitehaven to Edinburgh, 'in the custody of two constables as this unfortunate man had, for some days past, discovered such marks of insanity as made it advisable to remove him.'

Graham had for some years been devoting more of his time to an obsessional type of religious activity. His pamphlets and tracts at this time demonstrate characteristics suggestive of schizophrenia, and it has been put forward that Graham became a drug addict. In view of the strong ideas that he held with

E

reference to drugs, and there is good evidence in his writing
that he practised what he preached to his dying day, this would
seem to be unlikely. Whatever the precise diagnosis, it is
evident that Graham suffered from some form of mental derangement which steadily and progressively dominated him. And yet
he had relatively lucid intervals.

During his more sensible periods James was up to all his old
tricks again. Before he had left London, after the Temple of
Health closed, he introduced a new craze in an exhibition in
Panton Street, Haymarket. Henry Angelo's description of this
is worth while quoting in full. 'I was present at one of his
evening lectures on the benefits arising from earth-bathing (as
Graham called it), and in addition to a crowded audience of men,
many ladies were there to listen to his delicate lectures. In the
centre of the room was a pile of earth in the middle of which
was a pit where a stool was placed: we waited for some time
when much impatience was manifested, and after repeated calls
of "Doctor, Doctor!" he actually made his appearance "en
chemise." After making his bow he seated himself on the stool.
Then two men with shovels began to place the mould in the
cavity: as it approached to the pit of his stomach he kept lifting
up his shirt and at last took it entirely off, the earth being up to
his chin and the doctor being left in puris naturalibus. He then
began his lecture, expatiating on the excellent qualities of the
earth bath, how invigorating it was, etc. Quite enough to call
up the chaste blushes of the modest ladies. Whether it was the
men felt for the chastity of the female audience, or that they had
had quite enough of this imposing information, which lasted
above an hour, either the hearers got tired or some wished to
make themselves merry at the Doctor's expense and there was
a cry of "Doctor, a song!" The Doctor nodded assent and after
a few preparatory Hems, he sang or rather repeated,

> The fair married dames who so often deplore,
> That a lover once lost is a lover no more.'

He gave various similar exhibitions about the country until
1790. During the last few years of his life there is ample
evidence that Graham's mind was obsessed with religious
mania and that he was becoming, eventually, a victim of his
own tomfoolery. In his last pamphlet he signed an affidavit

dated 3rd April, 1793, 'that from the last day of December, 1792 to the 15th day of January, 1793 he neither ate, drank, nor took anything but cold water, sustaining life by wearing cut up turves against his naked body, and rubbing his limbs with his own nervous ethereal balsam.' The latter was one of his famous quack medicines originally dispensed at the Temple of Health. This was a feeble attempt to get back into the public eye. His health failed rapidly and he died at his house opposite the Archer's Hall in Edinburgh on the 26th June, 1794 from a sudden haemorrhage.

Getting such a flamboyant character as Graham into perspective is not easy. That he was an out and out Quack is of course fairly established. But he had qualities that distinguished him from the majority of his brethren.

First of all he had great personal courage. There is the evidence that he went as far afield as America to make his fortune in times when travel was a hazardous adventure. He also had the courage to gamble everything he had on what must have been a hunch when he established his Temples of Health. Graham also had a first-class brain. He could judge people and handle them adroitly. In London anyway his judgement seldom failed him. Scottish public opinion, incredibly enough he misjudged badly. Probably he had become too anglicised by 1783 to be sound in his assessment of the minds of his countrymen. Originality and foresight were well developed in Graham's personality and his ideas and teaching on hygienic and social problems were years ahead of his Age.

The opinion of orthodox medical practitioners on Quacks is always interesting. Apparently Graham, although dubbed a charlatan by most of the doctors, was much sought after for cures by members of the profession itself. One example is the case of Dr Glen. This Edinburgh character was a man not noted for his generosity. One of his few actions of public spirit was to present a bell for the local orphanage. (His fame was said thus to be sounded throughout the City.) Dr Glen was rather at a loss to know what to give Dr Graham in the way of a professional fee after he had cured him of an eye complaint. Some members of the Edinburgh Faculty suggested asking the 'good doctor' to dine at a fashionable tavern and presenting him with a purse containing 30 guineas. Dr Glen was privately assured that

Graham would decline the gift. To his chagrin Graham at once accepted it 'with a very low bow and graciously thanked him kindly.'

Graham's patients too demonstrated their gratitude for services rendered in most generous terms sometimes. For instance a rich foreigner gave him an annuity of £50 a year for life because his health had been so much improved after taking up the Graham régime. Unfortunately Graham's last years – marred by incipient insanity – showed his degeneration from an intelligent man to a crazy religious crank. He died in comparative penury before seeing his best ideas and theories bear fruit and bring him lasting fame.

7

THE HIDDEN FORCE

Graham, efficient quack as he was realised how much electrical
appliances impressed his patients. When Galvani demonstrated
in 1786 the way in which shocks from an electric machine would
make a frog's leg contract, many people felt that here was one of
life's mysteries solved. The idea was born that surely every
movement of every muscle, fine or gross was due to electricity.
The frenzied movements of a violinist's fingers, the palpitating
heart racing in the chest after exertion, or the languid lifting of
a beautiful woman's eyelids could all be expressed in terms of
electricity. Electricity was surely THE VITAL FORCE. Perhaps it
was the secret of life itself! Even today we do not understand
very much about the electricity of life so perhaps we can forgive
our 18th- and 19th-century forefathers for clutching many half-
baked electrical ideas close to their bosoms.

And yet for the majority of people the MAGIC of electricity
was probably its main fascination. The early classical demonstrations of static electricity were pretty impressive in a
theatrical way. A simple ebony rod, when rubbed with a cat's
fur or a silk handkerchief, became charged with electricity and
could pick up small pieces of paper, fragments of material, etc.,
as if by magic. Later, machines were invented that could build
up tremendous electro-static charges. Wimshurst's Friction
Machine was one of these. By the contrarotation of two discs at
high speeds a huge potential difference of electrical charges
could be established on adjacent metal electrodes. When this
electrical force became greater than the insulating properties of
the air between the electrodes, a spark or flame would leap
between them, probably accompanied by a sharp crack. Here

133

was the explanation of the noise of thunder and the flash of lightning. Soon electric currents were demonstrated which passed along wires quite invisibly and turned small motors, electrolysed solutions or lit lamps.

The forces of magnetism are perhaps even more mysterious than those of electricity. They must have made a great impression on the 18th-century mind. In the 20th century, many problems, including the source of the earth's magnetic force, remain largely unsolved. If the 18th-century minds felt that electricity was the hidden force that controlled their destiny it is not fair to criticise them too arrogantly. Nevertheless some of their foibles have proved amusing and are instructive inasmuch as they may stop us making similar mistakes in our day and age.

As things have turned out electricity, from the medical point of view, has been a disappointment. X-rays, the electrocardiogram, and the electroencephalogram, have of course been a great boon diagnostically. And of more recent years the speciality of radiotherapy has made advances in the treatment of malignant diseases. Diathermy has given the surgeon an operating instrument that he can sometimes use in place of the scalpel. All these advances admittedly use electricity as their essence but as time has crept by it has become increasingly obvious that electricity has not fulfilled the hopes that its initial magic stimulated.

It is not a cure-all. But to the Quacks it remained with its obvious and easily demonstrated properties an endowment of immense wealth. The most amusing episodes in the exploitation of the Hidden Force occurred at the end of the 19th and the beginning of the 20th centuries. Sometimes the Quacks would rely on seemingly complicated electrical apparatus to impress their patients. Others merely exploited the invisible magic in the simplest possible way. They bottled it and sold it to gullible folk who should have known better.

One such genius was an Italian who styled himself Count Mattei. Just before the turn of the century this 'foreign nobleman' was doing extraordinarily well with three electrical remedies in London. So well that he organised agencies for the handling of his cures that he modestly claimed would 'cure cataracts, mend broken bones,' and 'remedy almost any ill that human nature is heir to.' He told an Agent, retailing his Cure, that he would not 'lack gold in millions. You will attract it as a magnet attracts iron. You have the magnet in your intelligence and your activity. Work with your ability and I guarantee a good result.' Unfortunately as things turned out the Count and his Agent fell out over the simple matter of discounts and the gold did not flow quite as was expected. Mattei's remedies were described as being advertised everywhere, 'in the newspapers, pamphlets, handbills, on walls, on omnibuses, bathing machines, and even on the sails of fishing boats.' They were to be seen alongside the railways and high up among the clouds by means of electrical flashes.' Selling at 3/9, for a small phial containing $\frac{3}{4}$ oz., they were obviously very popular. For a reason best known to their inventor they came in three forms.

These were Electricita Bianca, Verde, and Rossa. Perhaps the colours were something of a reflection on the birthplace of the count. (White, green and red are the main colours of the Italian flag). The editor of *Health News*, writing about the famous Electricities in 1896, suggested that the green variety might be so named as a 'delicate compliment to the Count's admirers.' Following an article in the *National Review*, one of the consultants of the Royal Cancer Hospital was unsporting enough to send the three forms of The Electricities to a Public Analyst for a full electrical, magnetic and chemical investigation. The report was significant and crushing. The three solutions had no magnetic or electrical properties. Their colour (even the green and red 'Electricities' were actually white), odour, taste, polarity, specific gravity, chemical composition, indicated that they were composed of one substance and one substance alone – Water.

No wonder *Health News*' Editor commented that 'as soon as the money market has recovered from its low unspeculative condition, we shall expect to see in the financial papers an advertisement worded, "Wanted, a few persons to join a syndicate for the purchasing of water at 1/– per 1,000 gallons and retailing it at 5/– an oz." '

If the Count was on the way out another electrical craze was on the way in. The great era of the electric corset was at hand. Typical of them all, and there must have been hundreds of types for 'ladies, maids, girls and boys,' was the electric corset of

Mr C. B. Harness. Harness's – an unexpectedly apt name – ran
a big business making and selling electric corsets. Their headquarters was a fine four-storied building on a prominent
corner site at 52 Oxford Street, London.

Known as the Medical Battery Company Ltd, or sometimes
The Electropathic Institute, their advertisements were always
headed BY ROYAL LETTERS PATENT. Emblazoned over this was
the Royal coat of arms. Readers of the *Young Ladies Journal*
in the 1890's might well be excused believing that the Queen
herself wore one of the famous corsets. The facts of the matter
were quite different. In those days the British Government
realised some £250,000 yearly by a tax on articles designated
as patent medicines. All such articles carried the Government
stamp, BY ROYAL LETTERS PATENT, to prove that the tax had
been paid. Successful Quacks have always been good business
men. They soon realised that advertising capital could be made
out of this device.

The corset advertisements usually showed rather thoughtful
young women standing around negligently in décolleté chemises,
and well fastened into their electric corsets. From various spots
on their anatomy 'electric sparks' could be seen darting out.
Clearly the current was switched on! 'Ladies of all ages and in
all stations of life' were urged to 'procure at once one of Harness's
beautifully designed and scientifically constructed electrical
corsets.' They were, we are told, a boon to 'delicate women and
all who suffer from organic diseases, rheumatic affections, and
weak back. It will always do good, and never harm. There is no
sensation felt whatever wearing it, while benefit always and
quickly follows.' A classical and almost modern note is struck
in the assurance that it not only 'invigorates the entire system,'
but also, 'assists nature in the HEALTHY DEVELOPMENT OF THE
CHEST.'

The ladies seem to have been preoccupied with this as much
in the 1890's as they are in the 1960's. Not satisfied with this
selling point, Mr Harness also alleged that his corsets cured such
diverse ailments as 'functional irregularities,' (whatever they
may have been), 'hysteria, loss of appetite, dysepsia,' and most
ominous of all, 'internal complaints.' Of course, testimonials
from satisfied ladies formed a large part of the advertisements
for the electrical corsets. Many satisfied clients found that the

benefits of electricity were not exclusively feminine. For instance, a Mrs Horner of Enfield wrote: 'I used to suffer severely from a weak back and acute nervousness, but since wearing your electrical corset I have completely recovered. I would not be without them for a £100. My husband is as pleased as I am with the wonderful curative appliance, as he was thoroughly restored to health and vigour, etc.' This was the peak of the testimonial as well as of the corset age, and many corset makers' advertisements printed recommendations from named medical practitioners, specialists and members of the Peerage as a matter of course.

What did the public have to pay for a boon such as the Harness corset? Well, the manufacturer was anxious to place it within the reach of 'all classes of society.' They retailed at 5/6 each, post free, or two for 10/6. Were they cheap at the price? This must be a debatable point when one considers that at this time women could buy a silk umbrella for 2/6, a tailormade dress at 14/6, Siberian Squirrel Boas for 18/11, a Singer sewing machine for £1 12s 6d, and a fashionable sealskin jacket for £8.

On the other side of the Atlantic our American cousins were being treated to the same sort of benevolence by the Electric Appliance Company. They manufactured the Addisons Galvanic Electric Belt. Although this was suitable for treating ladies diseases (female pains), it was to men that their advertisements were mainly directed. Perhaps American society was less matriarchal in those days. Directness of approach is the key-word in American corset advertising. For instance 'If you are weak you need electricity – for lost womanhood and manhood there is nothing like electricity, it is the greatest power on earth. It puts life and force into anything it touches: gives relief to rheumatism, backache, kidney, liver and bladder troubles, early decay, night losses, lack of nerve vigour, nervous debility, constipation, dyspnoea, underdevelopment, and lost vitality.' For this tremendous boon a mere $2.50 was asked.

Curiously not even the manufacturers took any pains to preserve a perfunctory faith in their product. A notice in a current 'Show Business' advertising paper, the *Billboard*, addressed to 'medicine showmen, agents, palmists and hustlers,' showed this nicely. It advertised that 'you are losing some nice easy money if you fail to work our high grade electric belts, appliances, body batteries. Also a nice sideline for performers making one to six days' stands, 500–1,000 per cent profit. The Electric Appliance Company Incorporated, 1891.' This is surely one of the frankest and most interesting confessions of Quackery of all time. The belt, made of strips of vivid yellow and red cotton, crudely made to include small pieces of copper and zinc, was sold to Quacks at $1.10 a dozen, to sell at $2.50 each.

Not all American belts and corsets were sold at such bargain prices. An American physician who worked at sick people's dispensaries mentions that some very poor patients who should have been spending all their available money on nourishment often appeared wearing expensive electric corsets. Some of these corsets, made of chamois leather, would retail at as much as $24 each.

If you did not fancy a belt or corset an electric medal was available. Advertisements for these appliances, merely made of a series of discs of different metals crudely stuck together, showed them hanging around the necks of strong looking, virile, bearded men. Electrical energy radiated from them in all directions (in the newspapers of course). In actual fact not one iota of electricity or magnetism with any therapeutic effect was produced in them at all. Any good they did was purely due to faith healing. The same might be said of any talisman or charm.

The history of Medicine and Folklore is full of references to such objects. Perhaps the most famous one of all gave Sir Walter Scott the title for his novel *The Talisman*. It will be remembered that this was about the Lee Penny, a dark red stone set in a silver coin of Edward IV's reign. Water, in which this penny had been dipped, became highly curative. At one time it had a great reputation. So much so that when the city of Newcastle was attacked with a great epidemic during the time of Charles I, the Lee Penny was borrowed from its owners, the Lockharts of Lee on the deposit of some £6,000.

It is interesting to read of primitive electric medals being in use prior to the 19th century. Naturally occurring magnets, known as lodestones, which attracted or repelled iron objects were known to the Ancient Chinese and Greeks. This apparently magical quality always fascinated mankind. There is an 18th-century report of Henry Hind Pelly, Esq., of Upton, Essex, wearing 'constantly a piece of lodestone, sewed in a little flannel case, suspended by a black ribbon around his neck next to his skin.' He was a gentleman of advanced years who said that he had read in an old book that the wearing of a magnet next to the skin was a sure preservative against gout. He managed to obtain 'one of the most powerful in the world, lodestone occurring in Golconda, and effected a successful cure for his troublesome illness.'

If the electric belts, corsets and medals owed their popularity to a mixture of talismatic magic and dubious electric theory, the electric rings so beloved by our grandfathers must have had an even greater appeal. Rings were much used by the ancients as practical therapeutic agents. One Roman physician, Marcellus, directed the patient who was suffering from a pain in the side, to wear a pure gold ring. It had to be inscribed with some Greek letters and put on the finger 'on a Thursday, at the decrease of the moon,' and to be worn on the same side as the patient was afflicted. A 4th-century physician, Trallian, cured the cholic and all bilious complaints with an octagonal ring of iron. Words engraved upon it commanded the bile to enter the body of a lark, and so fly away. Another ring used by this same physician was a cure for 'the stone.' It was copper and engraved with 'the lion, crescent, and star,' and had to be worn on the fourth finger. Early English ring cures include a cure for styes or sore eyes. 'For sore eyes, before sunrise, or shortly after it begins fully to set, go to the wort Proserpinae, and scratch it round with a gold ring and say that "thou wilt take it for leechdom of the eyes." '

Edward the Confessor was said to have given one of his rings to a poor man who begged for alms. It was returned to him some years later. It had gained an enormous reputation abroad as a cure for 'cramp and falling sickness' (epilepsy). From this arose, it is thought, the custom of hallowing rings on Good Friday. These were bestowed according to the ancient physician Andrew Boorde, 'without money or petition.' Struck in either precious or base metals they were distributed in this way by Henry VIII and subsequently by Queen Mary.

Generally when rings are given freely, as in marriage, people the world over believe them to be efficacious amulets and charms.

A curious mixture of religion and witchcraft is seen in the old English custom of Sacrament Rings. These were made of money collected in various ways, usually closely associated with the Church. Details vary in different parts of the country but a Cornish custom is fairly representative. A person suffering from paralysis or rheumatism would collect thirty pennies in the Church porch 'without asking for any.' The pennies were changed into a silver coin from the Offertory by the priest. Then the patient, hobbling into the church walked three times round the communion table. The silver coin would then be delivered to the local blacksmith who in turn made it into a ring. After three weeks of wearing this a cure could be expected. (There is evidence that the smiths who worked rings in this way were often dishonest and kept the silver, making them of something less precious.)

Another common ring cure was used for cramp. For this painful spasmodic condition, something very special was needed. Old coffin handles or nails that had been used to fasten up coffins were considered to be absolutely essential!

With such a background of folk medicine to work on it is no wonder that electric rings proved extremely efficacious to the Quacks. It would be impossible to give a full account of the electric rings that appeared on the market at the end of the last century. Characteristic of the species was the Electro-Chemical Company's famous product manufactured at Toledo, Ohio. This priceless piece of jewellery was practically given away for a paltry two dollars. For this modest sum a cure could be expected for twenty-two serious conditions including diabetes, uraemia, appendicitis, epilepsy and cancer. The rings were to be worn on the fourth finger of the left hand, 'as it is well known that a nerve, artery (or is it vein), is there that goes directly to the heart.' So went the manufacturers' instructions.

The theory behind the beneficial action of electric rings was simple if ingenious. Here it is. Disease is caused by acid in the blood. The action of the sweat from the finger, working on the metals in the ring, produces electricity. This neutralises the terrible internal acids and All Is Well. Disease is Cured! There are only two flaws in this theory from the scientific point of view. Firstly the diseases mentioned are not caused by acid in the blood, secondly the electric rings generated no electricity.

To this might be added that if any electricity had been generated it would have had no beneficial effect on the patient.

Evidence of these appliances 'drawing out disease' was alleged to be demonstrated by the deposits that occurred inside the ring and on the finger after they had been worn for a few hours. Unfortunately for the manufacturers the American Department of Agriculture and Bureau of Chemistry analysed a ring and found it composed of a commercial grade of iron. The deposit could be produced equally well on a piece of rolled up blotting paper as on a finger. It was, of course, simply rust. Strangely enough this is the only evidence of electrolytic activity ever demonstrated by electric rings. How successful the rings were in treating the diseases that they were supposed to cure can only be a subject for doubt and conjecture. How successful they were to the manufacturers is well known. The Electro-Chemical Ring Company alone sold some $45,600 worth of them in a year before they were convicted of 'obtaining money through the United States mails by means of false and fraudulent pretences, representations or promises.'

Being constantly alive to the possibilities of exploiting the frailties of human nature is a necessity for Quacks and hoodlums. W. C. Fields' dictum: 'Never give a sucker an even break,' might be adopted, unofficially of course, as the Quacks' motto. Should those who specialised in electrical cures have ever needed a coat of arms to go with the motto, electrical rings and belts could have featured as the dexter and sinister. The shield itself might carry many devices. Perhaps honour of place should go to a picture of Hercules Sanches 'Electropoise.'

Hercules Sanche will be remembered as a clever, if of course, completely immoral character, who realised that people would eventually tire of rings and corsets and would then turn to something more 'scientific' for their cures. Hercules nearly gave the game away as he described himself as the 'discoverer of the Law of spontaneous cure of disease.' Although lucid expression was not one of Hercules's strong points (he is known to have published a sentence containing 468 words in one of his pamphlets), this 'law' is easy to understand. It really means that many diseases cure themselves spontaneously. These were the sort of diseases that Dr Sanche was hoping to cure with his Electropoise and many of his subsequent inventions. Luckily for the gallant doctor he did not realise his gaff here. Neither apparently did his patients!

The Electropoise itself was a neat little gadget consisting of a small metal cylinder called the Polizer, made rather in the shape and size of a pocket torch. There was no bulb or lens at the end however. Instead a short piece of cord emerged. This was connected at its far end to a small disc mounted on an adjustable strap. It sold like hot cakes we are told, at 10 dollars a time. What could be expected in the way of therapy as the result of purchasing such an instrument? Dr Sanche had the answer here. 'The Electropoise applies the needed amount of electrical force to the system, and by its thermal action places the body in condition to absorb oxygen through the lungs and its pores.' Although he goes on in a similar vein for several more paragraphs there is enough here to work on. Anyone who felt inclined to open up the cylinder of the Electropoise could find out what was inside. A few seconds' work with a hacksaw cutting through what appeared to be regulation type gas pipe might reveal the secret of the Electropoise. But alas, the cylinder was empty!

Doctor Sanche's claims could have been easily refuted by anybody who tried. But nobody did. The Electropoise could not by its simple construction supply any electrical force. No electrical force must mean no thermal action. No human body absorbs any oxygen through its pores and anyone not absorbing oxygen through their lungs would be dead in a few minutes. Even in 1895 one would think that Q.E.D., might have been written here and a line drawn, but the facts prove otherwise.

Encouraged by the success of the Electropoise Dr Sanche invented the Oxydonor. This, he modestly claimed, would cure all forms of disease from headache to hydrophobia. Otherwise similar to the prototype this Mark 2 model had one important modification. The Polizer contained a stick of carbon. The increased cost of manufacture Sanche made good by a trifling adjustment to the retail price. He raised it from 10 dollars to 35 dollars! To operate the Oxydonor one merely attached the metal disc to one's wrist or ankle, placed the Polizer in a bowl of water (a goldfish bowl is shown in an advertisement), and relaxed while the Oxydonor did its good work.

Sanche showed some business qualities far in advance of his age.

Having established himself with a good (he had proved) product, he went about increasing sales in a way that has been copied by business men the world over. First of all he started an Accessory Market and secondly an Owners Club. Some of the accessories Sanche produced were almost as ingenious as they were fraudulent. Typical was the 'Novora.' This was to be used in any case where somebody who was using an Oxydonor shared a bed. Potentially this could almost double sales. It consisted of two metal plates and straps tied together with a piece of cord. The bedmates merely attached a plate on each of their ankles on retiring. During the day-time the cord was rolled up on a neat little metal frame and presumably put away in a safe place, well away from the children. Another accessory was a sort of two-way Oxydonor attachment. By using this two people could obtain treatment from the same machine.

The Owners' Club, known as the Fraternity of Duxanimae, must have been a dull affair with its dreary vows and subscriptions to Dr Hercules Sanche who was now describing himself as the 'only master of diseases on earth.' Dull or not, Members of the Fraternity were apparently enthusiasts as they even subscribed to 'convertible donations' that could be freely used by the doctor 'to the best advantage according to his own best judgement and discretion.' The popular song 'Nice work if you can get it' was not published until some thirty years or so later, but it might have given Dr Hercules Sanche a useful signature tune. In all probability Hercules did not live to hear this apt ditty played. There is evidence that he was still quacking in the late 1940's and 1950's in Canada and America. He had many imitators but none could quite hold a candle to this old rascal master of pipe and wire therapy.

A direct extension of Hercules's brand of quackery is that of another American Quack who 'invented' the I-on-a-co in the late 20's. The contrast between the two men is interesting for while Sanche used no electricity to produce his electrical cures, the inventor of I-on-a-co, Gaylord Wilshire used mains voltage to produce his. The two pieces of apparatus had one thing in common. Electricity was not in any way directly or remotely responsible for any sensations apparent or imagined that may have been experienced by the poor dupes that used them.

Gaylord Wilshire was an American in the grand manner of the

1920's. Onetime Socialist politician, advertising man, magazine editor, real estate developer, man of letters (correspondent with George Bernard Shaw), naturalist, explorer, and sharepusher, he suddenly decided to devote a few years at the end of his colourful, if rather bogus life, to graduating as a medical 'con man.'

The I-on-a-co, also referred to rather unkindly as the 'magic horse collar,' 'worked,' if such a verb can validly be used in this sense, by 'magnetising the iron of the blood.' The apparatus came in two parts, one functional and one demonstrative. The 'horse collar' part was a coil of insulated wire about 18 inches in diameter. This was the functional, therapeutic unit. Another tiny coil of wire, a mouse collar if you like, had a small electric light bulb wired in circuit. If the first coil was connected up to mains and the smaller coil was brought near to it the bulb of the latter would light up. This is a simple experiment that is used to demonstrate the fundamental property of induced electric currents and is well known to every schoolboy who has studied physics. Gaylord Wilshire's idea was that you simply replaced the mouse collar with a patient, switched on, and he would 'glow' with health.

By magic no less impressive than the illuminated mouse collar, testimonials started to roll into I-on-a-co files telling of cures for cancer, pernicious anaemia, gallstones and mental derangement. Clients, not the manufacturers, declared that it made 'the dumb talk and the deaf hear.' Later Wilshire extended his field of activities to include that of beautician. He 'cured' baldness with his machine and even advertised it as a sort of primitive permanent waver for hair. Wilshire made hay while the sun shone. An I-on-a-co radio programme was started. Sales boomed and Wilshire, who had been associated with one or two shaky financial deals before, prospered. But eventually public opinion turned. The 'Better Business Bureau' and the American Medical Association were making themselves heard and felt. Dissatisfied customers were being produced. Gradually the nationwide agencies and offices of I-on-a-co were closing and in September, 1927 before the final crash came, Wilshire, who was, his biographer tells us, 'standing on the brink of a new world,' died at the age of 66.

Horribly clever as they seem, Wilshire, Sanche and other

exploiters of medical electricity really were not all that original. The man who was responsible for the idea was born nearly a century before.

Small towns seem to be the natural breeding place for potential Quacks. Norwich, Connecticut, in 1741, saw the birth of Elisha Perkins, a man who was to become the prototype of all the electrical appliance Quacks to follow. Perkins came from a medical family. His father was an extremely well-known practitioner in the Connecticut area and did in fact perform all the 'capital operations in the colony.' Elisha started out to follow in father's footsteps. He acted as his father's assistant, which was common practice in those days in medical apprenticeship. He is thought to have graduated at Yale although there is no evidence that this was so. Whether or not he was a successful practitioner is a very debatable point. That he was an unusual man is certain. Six feet tall, 'of a remarkable symmetry of figure, most kindly, MAGNETIC, and generous to a fault,' was a contemporary description of him. An interesting sidelight on medical behaviour in the 1790's is a note by a biographer that Dr Perkins made his rather arduous rounds on horseback, 'without the aid of artificial stimulants, never making the use of ardent spirits.'

Apparently the hard drinking of rum in New England was practically a *sine qua non* of professional life at that time, as we hear of clergymen and deacons in the church 'putting in a good stock of rum for the winter,' rather in the same way as we might fill up our coal-cellars. The prospect of all the other doctors in New England fortifying themselves for their rounds with Medford rum is a fascinating one.

Perkins, however, would have none of this. He often travelled sixty miles on horseback to see a patient, and also filled his house with students, resident patients and lodgers. Even making full allowance for the customs of the times this would hardly be what one would expect if Perkins had been the really prosperous New England practitioner that we are led to believe by his biographers. In all probability he was merely a country doctor of no great clinical talent who was scraping a living in the midst of fierce competition before he hit on an idea that lifted him out of the rut of domestic general practice and made him a world famous figure.

Apart from being teetotal in an area where the smell of rum on the breath was the badge of professionalism Perkins had another curious trait. On his rounds he would often ask if he could lie down and rest in a patient's house after a consultation. He would give the patient his watch and ask to be wakened in five minutes. Should a kindly patient, impressed by the doctor's tiredness, permit him to sleep a few minutes more, Perkins would always, on waking, complain that oversleeping had completely spoilt the effect of his rest. There can be no scientific reason for this. Obviously Perkins was a man with obsessional ideas and very susceptible to self-deception in the form of auto-suggestion.

Perkins' fame rests fair and square on his famous Metallic Tractors. Just how and when these were 'invented' remains in doubt. We are told he had noticed that when muscles and nerves were touched with metal objects spasmodic contractions sometimes took place. Evolving this as a theory to explain the rationale of Metallic Tractors is, of course, completely incomprehensible. Anyway, sometime during 1796 the famous Metallic Tractors were launched on an unsuspecting public.

Perkins originally made them in a tiny secret forge hidden in his house. The Tractors were alleged to be made of various metals, Gold and Platinum being mentioned. They were about 4 inches long and tapered slightly to a blunt end. One uninhibited contemporary observer likened them to the nails used in the fixing of horseshoes. It is difficult to see at first just how the Tractors caught on, especially when one considers that the particular area where Perkins lived has been called the 'Wooden Nutmeg State.'

Connecticut has been described as the place where the hard-headed type of American business man was originally spawned. The story of wooden nutmegs being manufactured in Connecticut to be sold elsewhere in America at 'spice prices,' is obviously apocryphal. But there is no doubt at all that the inhabitants of New England at this time were no country hicks who would be easily duped with a quack remedy, and yet they happily swallowed the theory of Tractors and 'Tractoration.'

Before long amazing cures were being attested. Although initially the Tractors were advertised modestly by Perkins, for 'pains in the head, face, teeth, breast, stomach, back, rheumatism, and all joint pains,' other more serious conditions such as 'paralysis, lameness and deformities of all types,' were soon being cured by the new magic.

The method of treatment was simplicity itself. The two Tractors were held together at their points and then drawn over the affected part of the body – always in the direction of downwards or outwards. The reverse direction of application was thought to be dangerous in the extreme. Sometimes the patients, if they had a delicate constitution, could not endure such a powerful force as Tractoration for the advised length of time, that is twenty minutes per day. In these cases caution was advocated and a limited Tractoration at intervals of two or three days was ordered. Strangely enough although Perkins' Tractors succeeded quickly in America and several high up personages in the country were soon recommending their use, including high court judges, diplomats and university professors (George Washington himself was said to have bought a pair), his professional colleagues were not impressed. In 1796 the Connecticut Medical Society censured Perkins and in 1797 they expelled him from their membership. This professional criticism did not daunt Perkins who was now selling vast numbers of Tractors at about £10 pair to the general public. (Half price for the medical profession and free to the Clergy).

The initial craze in America soon started to wane and shrewd Elisha realised that something new would be needed to fall back upon when Tractors sales began to lessen. This proved to be his eventual undoing for he announced that he had invented a new antiseptic cure for Yellow Fever. In 1799 there was a Yellow Fever epidemic in New York and Perkins, with the same obsessional enthusiasm that he had had for his Tractors, went to the city to demonstrate the efficacity of his new cure. Unfortunately, he in turn caught Yellow Fever and died of it within four weeks of going to New York.

If the therapeutic sun was beginning to set on Tractoration in the New World things were only just starting to move in the Old. A Danish diplomat's wife had bought a pair of Tractors while her husband was working in New York. She took them back to Denmark with her. Moving in diplomatic circles in Denmark and having such a unique cure with her for all the imaginary ailments of her set, the Tractors were soon adopted in a big way. Other countries were not to be left out of this amazing new therapy and soon books were being published in German on the use of Metallic Tractors in the treatment of various diseases.

Before his father died, Perkins's son was entrusted with the honour of introducing the previously exclusive American cure to the inhabitants of these Islands. As he so diffidently said himself, 'the writer has crossed the Atlantic and become resident in London, that he may devote his time and attention to the diffusion of this important discovery, and its application to the relief of the miseries of mankind.'

The metropolis welcomed him with open arms and he was soon importing his Tractors in sets of 200 at a time. He established himself in John Hunter's old house at 18 Leicester Square, where he attended patients daily every morning until 2.30 p.m., when he left to visit 'patients abroad.' He also had a sort of agency in Holborn where Ogilvy & Sons, book-sellers, handled the new magic at a substantial discount to themselves. Perkins was not slow to appreciate the value of getting into Spa towns. He soon entered into a business relationship with a surgical contact, Mr Longworth, at 11 Bond Street, Bath. Interest was so great that in 1797 Perkins Jnr, published his first book, *The Influence of Metallic Tractors on the Human Body in removing various Painful, Inflammatory diseases, such as rheumatism, pleurisy, some gout affections, etc., etc.* This book was an immediate success and went through several editions. The main contents were merely a collection of testimonials as to the efficacity of the Tractors in treating various diseases.

Typical was one of Longworth's, about a servant of Dr Fellows (Physician to H.R.H. Prince of Wales), who severely sprained his ankles. The Tractors were applied to the swollen part. This made the servant feel 'sick and faint,' which was welcomed as a sign of 'impending cure.' Sure enough half an hour later the patient was cured and could go about his business.

Just after the turn of the century the Tractors were doing so splendidly in England that a body of eminent men suggested that the boon of Tractoration should not be excluded from the impecunious. They felt it should be available to all, rich and poor alike. This might be cynically described as the dawn of socialised medicine in England. Perkins, of course, agreed. As

long as someone was going to pay he did not mind who it was.
And so the Perkinean Institution was formed in 1803. It had
premises in Frith Street, Soho. The President was none other
than the Right Honourable Lord Rivers. Governor Franklin
(son of Benjamin Franklin) and Sir William Barker were among
eleven eminent Vice Presidents. The opening of the Institution
where the sick poor could be treated free was celebrated by a
fine public dinner, held at the Crown & Anchor, Soho on the
15th July, 1803. Later several other provincial branch offices
of the Institution were opened, including one in Durham under
the patronage of the Bishop of St Davids.

For some time it looked as though there was to be no holding
Perkins. He declared that by 1804 over 5,000 cases had been
published that demonstrated the therapeutic effect of his
Metallic Tractors. He estimated that for every published case,
some 300 cures would have been wrought and gone unnoticed.
In true quack tradition he therefore multiplied his successes to
a mere one and a half million cures! Not content with this he
started to 'puff' the Tractors for curing diseases in horses and
dogs. This was a great success and soon both Madame's lap-
dog and the Squire's favourite nag were experiencing the benefits
of the 'Great American Invention.'

Eventually, perhaps as the result of the Perkins Institutions,
complaints started to be made about the Tractors. It is an
interesting facet of human nature that if people pay for something they will believe in it more firmly than if they get it for
nothing. Similar instances occur today. While patients will often
take medical advice that they pay for in Harley Street, when they
get it gratuitously, quite possibly from the same specialist under
the National Health Service, it is somehow less effective.

John Corry, writing his *Quack Doctors Dissected*, produced a
scathing attack on Perkins. He wrote, 'armed with twin
skewers, see Perkins, by main force drag the foul fiend from
Christian and from Horse.' Elsewhere in the country others
took up the cudgels. In Avondale near Stratford-on-Avon lived
a rich farmer called Thomas Wilkinson. He was a man of very
strong views. He did not like doctors much as he quoted
Dryden as saying 'God never made his work for man to mend.'
He also advised people to 'throw physic to the dogs, I'll have
none of it.' Bonesetters he had some time for ('a man who can

bind up a fracture is of real ability.') Quacks he absolutely abhorred.

One day he decided to give a dinner on the bowling green in front of his house to educate his villagers in the matter of Quackery. After one or two experiments on popular nostrums he turned his attention to the famous Tractors. Addressing his audience, 'you do not know how much your own health depends on the success of my experiments today,' he produced a pair of Tractors. They were not a genuine pair. Unknown to his audience he had had them forged by the local blacksmith out of an old kitchen poker. Mr Wilkinson then enquired of his audience for volunteers to come forward who were suffering from rheumatics. Dame Thomson presented herself with 'a pain in her arm.' 'We'll soon remove that,' said the farmer, 'here are a pair of the famous Metallic Tractors you have so often heard of. They cure all pains!' He then applied the Tractors and the patient soon announced herself cured. 'With a laugh,' Wilkinson 'ordered his house dog to be brought forward.' 'Poor Pompey' was produced, and the farmer directed one of his servants to 'sear the animal's foot with a red-hot iron, so that he might prove the efficacity of the tractors curing a burn.' (This was one of the wide claims of the Perkins Metallic Tractors). Although he used the genuine American model this time, poor Pompey 'yelped and wailed most horribly and soon fled to his kennel.' After this he told the audience of his deception. Experiments such as these would not have pleased the R.S.P.C.A. had they existed at the time, but they certainly impressed the locals to whom they were directed.

The sands of time for Perkins Jnr were fast running out. Several doctors up and down the country were publishing cures using Mock Tractors that were equally impressive clinically as Perkins's own testimonials. One of these was Dr John Haygarth of Bath. He made some tractors of wood and painted them to resemble 'real' tractors. His technique was to describe geometric figures on the patient's anatomy with the Tractors, while talking pseudo-scientific mumbo jumbo to a colleague. He carried out many fantastic 'cures' in this way quite easily. The most difficult thing he said was keeping a straight face during Tractoration. 'We were almost afraid to look at each other, lest an involuntary smile should remove the mask from our face.'

Another wily practitioner, Mr Richard Smith, a surgeon at Bristol Infirmary, also published various 'cures.' His Tractors were 'two tenpenny nails' coated with red and black sealing wax. One of his patients was a man called Edmund Williams. On the face of it this case should have been a failure. The 'poor, feeble subject' suffered from incontinence of urine. He expressed himself 'willing to try anything for a cure,' and Mr Smith gingerly applied the bogus tractors to various points on his pelvis. The patient responded immediately. 'I begin to feel something jumping up in my inside,' he said. Later he experienced 'smarting in his loins, and warmth in his skin.' After the treatment, he said, 'Yes, I am better, when I used to sit down, there was always a spurt of water come from me, but now I can prevent it.' Such was the power of mind over matter.

Gradually people began to realise there was no electrical or any other magic about the Tractors. It is incredible that many thousands of people, among them eminent members of the Professions, University Graduates, and Professors, convinced themselves of the efficacity of two metal rods about the size of pencils. Day by day with more and more adverse publicity building up, Tractoration was on the wane. By 1810 the Tractors were 'out.' Those that had used them were trying to forget them. Great men who had praised them regretted their enthusiasm and perhaps their gullibility. Perkins himself slipped quietly away back to his native land, richer it is said by some £10,000 most of which had been earned, to quote Johnson, in 'London, the needy villains general home.'

8

THE TESTIMONIAL BUSINESS

A Testimonial is to the Quack what a reputation is to more ethical practitioners. It would be difficult to imagine a more effective form of publicity than the testimonial, springing as it does, from the personal recommendation of a fellow man or woman. Not only does the product in question get a tremendous lift but the testator himself obtains a certain notoriety and publicity. As the *Toronto Star* once quoted 'if your brains won't get you into the papers, try a patent medicine testimonial, maybe your kidneys will!' The weakness of testimonials is a subtle thing, not liable to be appreciated by the uninitiated. It belongs to the 'after it, therefore because of it,' type of reasoning that can be very seductive if cleverly presented.

An example quoted in an article on the subject by the late Dr Arthur J. Cramp, gives an inkling as to how a testimonial may be born. A naïve young Christian Scientist testified that a litter of cats had been born at her house all completely blind. As a result of her attentions, with due reference to her particular beliefs, this terrible omission on the part of the Maker had been put to rights and ·eventually the poor creatures had been released from their life of darkness! If the public's knowledge of cats was as abysmal as it is over the natural history of disease then the miraculous cure of poor pussy's blindness might have made a good testimonial for Christian Science.

Things are not always what they seem to be at first sight. Most of us at times feel a little jaded, the world has not been running right for us. There has been trouble at the office, or the back axle of the car has been making 'expensive' noises. We wake in the morning feeling tired and depressed. To make matters worse a letter from the tax man arrives or the rates fall due. We rapidly feel much worse. In this state of mind our eye may fall on a newspaper advertisement that describes our plight exactly. Someone else has experienced our troubles. He has, lucky fellow, found salvation in this pill or that tonic and we wonder if it will do the trick for us. On the spur of the moment we buy some, and within a few days all is well. The clouds have rolled away. The tonic has worked. We are in the frame of mind to write a testimonial. In our enthusiasm we have overlooked that things have settled down at the office, the boss is pleased with us, the noise on the car was due to want of proper lubrication, and some shares we had forgotten suddenly paid a bumper dividend.

And yet, if we wrote a testimonial it is doubtful if it would be any good. It would probably contain too much or too little. To be fully effective the testimonial must be well edited and substantiated, a fact well known to a gentleman called Valentine Greatrakes, a master quack of the 17th century.

Greatrakes, born in County Waterford, Ireland, in 1628, had a large number of famous patients during his heyday. He was, a contemporary tells us, 'possessed of some peculiar temperament and as his body was composed of some particular ferments, sometimes by a light, sometimes by a violent friction, he repairs the temperament of the debilitated part, regenerating the blood and dissipating the heterogenous ferments out of the bodies of the diseased by the eyes, mouth, hands and feet.'

Greatrakes's testimonials were classics. They are well composed, quite obviously by himself, and are often testified by eminent medical and scientific authorities. One of the most famous of these was Robert Boyle. The fundamental weakness of them all is that they testify to the cure of the patient but do not necessarily define the condition, before Greatrakes gave his treatments.

Two typical examples are as follows. (1) Eleanor Dickinson's certificate.

Eleanor Dickinson of Clerkenwell, widow aged 45 years, or thereabouts, having been troubled with an exceeding tympany in her belly for the space of twelve years past, and used all means possible for her health, insomuch that prosecution thereof cost her above £60, but was altogether ineffectual. The 16th of this instant, April, she came to Lincoln's Inn Field, the place where Mr Valentine Greatrakes used to lay his hands on the diseased, but not being able to come near him by reason of the throng she snatched some of his urine and drank it, some of which she also put into her ears, which were so stopped she could not hear, and immediately she heard the noise of the people all around her: then going home, some hours after, the same urine began to work in her belly, and she voided in a pond four gallons of water, with a great quantity of wind at her privy part: and at her belly which was before two yards in compass, doth not now exceed three quarters of a yard. She likewise saith that at the same time she vomited out of her mouth several pieces of thick skin drawn over with blue veins, like to a fresh bladder, so that she now confesses herself to be completely cured and hath ascertained this as a truth under her own hand, April 21st, 1666. Signed Eleanor Dickinson in the presence of us who saw her. Albertus Otto Fahers, James Fairclough, M.D., Thomas Poaley, M.A.

(2) The testimonial of Ann Kelly.

Ann Kelly of Shalingate in the parish of Old Windsor, 21 years old, hath had the dead palsy fourteen years on her right side, not able to go, nor lift up her hand to her head. She was first touched by Mr Greatrakes at the beginning of April, 1666, who found ease the first day she was touched and so got strength more and more every day and now being the 26th April, 1666, she goes well without help of any stick, and hath very good use of her right arm, heretofore useless: only she goes as if her right leg were somewhat shorter than her left. Examined 26th April, 1666, by Robert Boyle, W. Smith, G. Denton, M.D., and James Fairclough, M.D.

A book entitled *A brief Account of Mr Valentine Greatrakes and Divers of the Strange Cures by him lately Performed*, was published in 1666. The testimonial section of the book runs into some fifty-one closely written pages. Strange cures is an apt description of most of them. Eventually Greatrakes fell on evil times and returned to his home town in Ireland to die in obscurity.

Some people found that the best way to handle the testimonial problem was to apply the principle of do it yourself. An Eno's Fruit Salts testimonial written in the 1890's went a bit too far. An advertisement appearing at the time of a typhoid epidemic in London stated, 'I used my Fruit Salt freely in my last attack of fever, and have every reason to say it saved my life,' J. C. Eno. It is doubtful if such a poignant personal reminiscence cut much ice, but other operators were less ingenuous in their approach.

George H. Mayr was one of these. He specialised in what might be called the 'given up by doctors' routine. His wonderful remedy for stomach troubles was popular in the United States at the turn of the century. This was not to be wondered at considering George's advertising technique. He merely provided the editors of various newspapers with a list of testimonials headed by the caption, 'Old Blank Resident Given up by Physicians.' He then tersely instructed the various editors concerned to 'insert name of city in heading each ad.' The resulting epic was therefore, 'Old Kentucky resident,' etc. The only limit to the number of residents so heartlessly deserted by their local medical men was the length of Mr Mayr's purse. It is surprising that so many newspaper editors co-operated in this shady business. George Mayr wrote his own copy. If it has been judged severely he had only himself to blame.

Another American firm decided to put their business in the hands of an agency. This firm did not sell quack medicines but a sort of do-it-yourself course of remedial exercises alleged to put everything right by a little chiropractic activity. The agency hit on the idea of the famous Colonel Bemis advertisements. Headed 'Bride and Groom' the copy showed an elderly yet sprightly bridegroom with his youthful and attractive bride, who was quoted as saying, 'the colonel may look his age but by all that's remarkable he doesn't act it, nor feel it, if his enthusiasm is any indication.' The obvious question (enthusiasm for what) is left unanswered. But the advertisement had just the right appeal as far as health and sexual rejuvenation were concerned. It certainly sent many a dollar rolling.

Unfortunately for the manufacturers, the American Federal Trades Commission unmasked Colonel Bemis as a jewellery salesman who filled in with a little professional modelling. Both the gallant colonel and his 'bride' admitted, rather unkindly perhaps, that they had never heard of the course of treatment that their pictures were advertising.

As the 20th century progressed the gratuitously received testimonial so prized by the advertisers was gradually replaced by the even more powerful purchased endorsement. Ace of the testimonial world was Doc Hartman, founder of the Peruna Company, described in Chapter 10. By means fair or foul he obtained testimonials from prominent soldiers, sailors, architects, clergymen, physicians and United States senators. Characteristically he did not ignore the small fry. Once he had a testimonial and his method of obtaining them was rather suspect, he followed up his catch with a continuation project. A letter was regularly sent to testators asking about their health and habits and enquiring if they still used Peruna. On receipt of an answer to these and other personal questions the Peruna company paid out the useful if diminutive sum of 25 cents.

Another American product that compared favourably with Peruna alcoholically was Paines Celery Compound. This contained 20 per cent alcohol, together with an insignificant amount of other drugs, and was immensely popular. Paines also managed to obtain favourable testimonials from quite a few important people. A very useful one came from Sarah Bernhardt. She confessed that Paines Celery Compound was 'the most powerful nerve strengthener that could be found.' Needless to say her opinion was backed by many, including prominent teetotallers and civic dignitaries.

Eventually manufacturers of quack medicines began to realise the potentialities of exploiting the sporting world. A general tonic and body builder called Nuxated Iron which the American Medical Association later described as containing practically no Nux (Nux Vomica, a popular form of strychnine used in tonics), and very little iron, had already obtained endorsement from a handful of retired Generals and Judges. A testimonial from the Vatican itself was claimed to come from Pope Benedict XV. Not wanting to rest on these laurels the manufacturers of Nuxated Iron signed on a formidable array of athletes to endorse their wares. Thus Jack Dempsey, after he had knocked out Jess Willard was quoted as saying 'Nuxated Iron put him in such superb condition and had helped him to whip Jess.' (Jess had presumably fallen down on his doses as he had previously been a Nuxated Iron champion himself). Dempsey's subsequent victories in the ring over Carpentier, Gibbons and Firpo were all hailed as Nuxated Iron victories. Eventually when Gene Tunney finally relieved Jack of his Champion's Crown fair play was presumably admitted as Tunney was endorsing Nujol as a 'rub down and regulator.'

Going on a little further in the investigation of sponsorship of medical nostrums gives us the fascinating story of Buffalo Lithia water. This product was a 'special' mineral water. Its popularity was due to a series of medical misbeliefs and mistakes, unparalleled in the history of Quack medicine. Two fallacies were widely believed in the 1920's, both by the public and by some of the profession. The first of these was that uric acid in excess in the body causes a large number of diseases, including rheumatism. The second was that Lithium salts would dissolve uric acid deposits out of vital tissues and reverse the bad effects of its accumulation.

We now know that these two beliefs are absolute nonsense, but supposing they were true then the medicine or Spa water containing Lithium would certainly be very useful in the treatment of rheumatism. A Professor of Medicine of the College of Physicians and Surgeons, New York, and a Vice President of the American Medical Association, stated 'Buffalo Lithia water is strikingly superior to emergency solutions of Lithia tablets and pure water, even when the said solution is an exceedingly strong one.' A member of the faculty of medicine at Paris was quoted as saying, 'In the class of cases in which Lithia, soda and potash are especially indicated, I have obtained far better results from the Buffalo Lithia water than from any of the preparations of Lithium of the Pharmacopœia.' The Pope's physician, a member of the Academy of Rome alleged 'Buffalo Lithia water, by its richness of composition with Lithia is of marvellous efficacity in cases of gout and chronic articular and muscular rheumatism.'

The incredible thing is that when some rather sceptical chemists of the Department of Agriculture at Washington analysed Buffalo Lithia water they found that it contained practically no Lithium salts at all! In fact they stated that there was more Lithium, volume for volume, in straight Potomac river water than in the celebrated remedy, and that to get one single therapeutic dose of Lithium it would be necessary to drink some two hundred thousand gallons of 'Buffalo Lithia water.' In other words the enthusiastic testimonials of the eminent doctors were not only mistaken with regard to the therapeutic effects of Lithium but had supported a completely bogus product.

The lesson of Buffalo Lithia water has been only slowly learnt by the Medical Profession. Although glowing Testimonials of the type quoted are not seen today, small series case reports are often written up in reputable Journals and quite erroneous conclusions are drawn from them. In many of these articles the principles of scientific investigation have been forgotten and impressions have been substituted. These have sometimes given this or that drug a short period of fame before it has been later rejected into pharmacological obscurity.

Strange as it may seem investigators agree that the majority of Testimonials given to, and quoted by, manufacturers are quite genuine articles. When they were written the faith in the remedy was there. Unfortunately, enquiry men often followed up the Testimonial to see what happened to the testator. This produced some instructive if rather depressing information. For example one young woman who announced herself cured of tuberculosis died of the disease a year prior to the time that her Testimonial was being used by her Quack Doctor. The makers of a Californian cure for Diabetes and Bright's disease published many Testimonials. Unfortunately the cases followed up by Dr Cramp showed that all the testators had, within months, died of Diabetes or Nephritis. The Bureau of investigation of the American Medical Association went to work with customary thoroughness on a large number of claims of remedies for Cancer, Tuberculosis and other serious diseases, and eventually produced a file index which included the Testimonials and the death certificates of the testators! Certificates frequently noted death from diseases claimed to be cured.

Very occasionally, chance refuted a Testimonial. An example of this was one from a local resident printed in the same edition of a newspaper that carried his obituary notice. Perhaps some unlucky accident such as this and the increasing activity of Medical Associations all over the world finally dissuaded manufacturers from using the testimonial technique quite so frequently. Refuting bogus cures had become a popular business, particularly when it was possible to get some concise proof of dishonesty.

An interesting squabble occurred over Clarke's Blood Mixture. This was advertised by Testimonials in a big way, the veracity of which were rather questionable. A public analyst of eminence, Dr Alfred Swain Taylor, F.R.S., published the formula of Clarke's Blood Mixture and commented adversely on its use and safety. The only active ingredient present in the medicine was potassium iodide. This has a definite pharmacological action as will be described, but it has no beneficial effect on the blood, and could in no way support the maker's claims.

The effects of iodine on the human body are legion. It is used with some effect in the treatment of certain goitres. It tends to liquefy the sputum and is sometimes included in the more stimulating type of cough mixture. In doses that vary from person to person it is capable of producing the symptoms of Iodism. These make rather unpleasant reading. To quote from an authoritative Materia Medica, Iodism symptoms include 'an objectionable metallic taste in the mouth, nasal congestion with a profuse watery excretion from the nasal mucosa, redness of the conjunctiva and lacrimation, pain over the frontal sinuses, swelling and redness of the gums, palate, and fauces, accompanied by a profuse salivation, a coated and raw tongue, aching in the temperomandibular joints and skin rashes of an acneiform or pustular type.'

The adverse publicity which the blood mixture received as a result of Dr Alfred Swain Taylor's report gave delight to certain members of the Medical Profession who were spending quite a lot of time and money refuting quack medicines. Imagine their chagrin therefore, when a few years afterwards large advertisements started to appear in the London newspapers stating, 'Clarke's Blood Mixture is entirely free from Any Poison or Metallic Impregnation, does Not Contain any Injurious Ingredients and is a Good, Safe and Useful Medicine.' Signed Alfred Swain Taylor, F.R.S.

Such a contradiction (published incidentally, posthumously), from a worthy member of the Royal Society, was rather too much to swallow, and the editor of a popular medical journal (*Health News*), posed four questions to Mr Clarke. (1) Where, when and under what circumstances did Dr Swain Taylor give the alleged testimonial? (2) By whom was his signature witnessed? (3) When and where can the original be inspected? (4) Why did the proprietors of the Blood Mixture withhold from public knowledge so important a Testimonial until years after Dr Taylor's death?

They received no answers, however, and the whole matter might have been buried in the limbo of unsolved controversies, but for the declaration of a certain Dr H. C. Barlett. Dr Swain Taylor had been an old friend of his. Dr Barlett was a dying man when he contacted the editor of *Health News* and told him the following story. While he had been visiting a friend in the city, Mr Clarke had arrived. Dr Barlett's host baited Clarke about the adverse effect of Swain Taylor's original report on the reputation of his product. It was clear that Clarke had been trying to get a favourable Testimonial from Dr Swain Taylor without success, for he laughed and said, 'I shall wait a few years till the old fogey is dead, and then no one can prove that he did not give me a certificate.'

This in fact he did, applying the old dictum that if you want a really good Testimonial, write it yourself. This was not the end of Clarke's Blood Mixture as for many a long year the pamphlet enclosed around the bottle advised buyers that 'No matter what the symptoms may be, the real cause of a large proportion of all diseases is bad blood. Clarke's world-famed Blood Mixture is not recommended to cure every disease: on the contrary, there are many that it will not cure, but it is a guaranteed cure for all blood diseases. It never fails to cure Scrofula, Scurvy, Glandular Swellings and Sores, Cancers or Ulcers, Bad Legs, Secondary Symptoms, Syphilis, Piles, Rheumatism, Gout, Dropsy, Blackheads or Pimples on the Face, Sore Eyes, Eruptions of the Skin and the Blood, and Skin Diseases of every Description.'

The label still announced 'the mixture is pleasant to the taste, and warranted free of anything injurious to the most delicate constitution of either sex, which all pills and most medicines sold for the above diseases contain.' In other words, Iodism – never heard of it! The estimated cost of the ingredients of Clarke's Blood Mixture was less than 1/25th of its retail price, and so even if gross sales gradually dwindled, net profits would still remain reasonably high.

Testimonials can sometimes backfire rather nastily as the manufacturers of Mother Seigel's Syrup found out. The famous syrup was primarily introduced as an indigestion cure, but the splurge on the wrapper did not leave any doubt in the mind that it did much more than this. It 'purified the blood system and had a highly specific action on the stomach, liver and kidneys.' It was described as being purely vegetable but an analysis by the British Medical Association chemists showed that it contained hydrochloric acid (hardly a vegetable compound). It also contained a little capsicum and some aloes. Treacle and water made up the largest proportion of its in-

The Old Keeley Institute 'shot tower'

In tights I
was a sight
at 204 lbs.

Texas Guinan—a
sight in tights

*American Medical
Association*

gredients by far. Such a mixture had absolutely no effect on indigestion or indeed any therapeutic effect on the stomach, liver or kidneys. Mother Seigel's Syrup had one saving grace in that it was innocuous and unlikely to cause much trouble to its manufacturers if they kept their mouths shut. Unfortunately, patent medicine manufacturers cannot do this.

A reasonably well-known Manchester physician, Dr Dacre Fox, had his name very freely used, in an unflattering light, in a widely advertised Mother Seigel's Syrup testimonial. Seigel's made the fatal mistake of believing that Dr Fox had died. In actual fact he had merely moved house. Good for him, he was soon busy with his lawyers suing Seigel's Syrup proprietors for libel. At the trial, in a Leeds court, £1,000 damages were awarded to Dr Fox. Seigel's appealed against this and eventually the case came to the Lords of Appeal.

Mr Justice Lindley giving judgment observed 'that the defendant had published the libel under the impression that the plaintiff was already dead, and that they would be perfectly safe, inasmuch as the person libelled was dead and could not turn up against them. Unfortunately for them, Dr Fox was alive and instituted an action. The defendants tried to justify the libel which they unquestionably failed to do. There was little evidence to show that Dr Fox had been guilty of the conduct which they imputed to him. The whole object of the libel was to puff the defendants' wares and they went out of their way to libel the plaintiff for the purpose of puffing their own quack medicines. They were utterly unscrupulous as to the means taken by them, so unscrupulous that they did not shrink from casting blame on the person supposed to be dead. The Court saw no reason to grant either a new trial or reduce the damages: therefore the appeal would be dismissed with costs.'

The whole case must have cost the Mother Seigel's Syrup proprietors many thousands of pounds. Doubtless they could afford it. A three ounce, 2/6 bottle, of the famous Syrup, cost them about 1/3rd of a penny to fill – a profit ratio almost impossible to calculate.

Recent examples of the 'paid handout' included a favourite panel game personality who was renowned for his testiness and irritability. In his endorsements he used to admit to ill-treating his stomach and his rather choleric temperament seemed to

F

support this admission. Many chronic dyspeptics must have been persuaded to seek relief in the remedy so confidently recommended.

This advertisement must have paid off very well judging by the frequency with which it has been repeated. On the whole, however, the majority of popular personalities in the sporting and theatrical worlds have limited themselves to advertising cigarettes, beauty products and hair creams. Perhaps, they feel, that to give a patent medicine Testimonial is now just not done.

More than occasionally the Medical Profession has itself contributed to the Testimonial racket during recent years. Just after the war a large number of British doctors were presented with a dozen bottles of Guinness by the manufacturers. Their spontaneous thanks for this generous gift provided many a Guinness advertisement with a quote from an M.B. Some doctors composed amusing poems in praise of the 'tonic effect' of Guinness which made good 'endorsements' from the Medical Profession. The Americans had pioneered this idea with their Lucky Strike campaign before the war. A packet of a hundred cigarettes sent to American doctors, together with a questionnaire on the merits or otherwise of the cigarettes produced the 'Lucky Strikes do not affect the Throat' slogan that was endorsed by physicians all over America.

But gradually in America and elsewhere the Testimonial business was becoming less popular. In England, the Cancer act of 1939 and the Pharmacy and Medicines act of 1941 had made it illegal to mention certain illnesses, such as Cancer, Diabetes and Tuberculosis in advertising matter. The new British Code of Standards in Medicine and Treatments in 1950 was another nail in the coffin of the Testimonial Advertiser. The standards were drawn widely in terms that prevented false claims being made and almost overnight many 'old faithfuls' of the Testimonial World disappeared for ever on posters and in the press.

9

LET'S JOIN THE LADIES

Were women the First Doctors? It certainly looks as though they may have been. Although no one can tell for sure, presumptive evidence points that way. Anthropologists who investigated the aboriginal races that existed until recent times under conditions approximating to Stone and Bronze Age life, think that the ladies led the field as far as primitive medicine was concerned. For instance, the Californian Indians had a Medicine Woman who took her patients to a lonely place, gave them a 'sweat and pummelling,' and sucked the disease out of their mouths and placed it in a basket to be taken home. The Aztecs and certain African tribes also favoured Medicine Women in their early civilisations.

Gradually as ancient man became less involved with hunting and fighting and concerned himself with more intellectual pursuits, he probably annexed doctoring as a predominantly male activity. Even in the third and fourth centuries B.C., in Greece there is evidence that women doctors were becoming less popular. A smear campaign was once engineered that branded them all as suspected abortionists. A famous Grecian lady doctor called Agnodice went so far as to wear men's clothes and dress her hair as a man so as to escape notoriety and suspicion. Unfortunately rivals were soon after her and had her tried for practising under false pretences. Her satisfied women patients came to her aid and lobbied 'you are not our husbands but our enemies if you condemn our Agnodice who saves our lives.' Under such pressure male judicial opinion wavered and Agnodice was allowed to continue her practice unhindered.

Fame as a Physician in ancient times did not necessarily bring personal happiness. Octavia, who studied medicine in Rome, brewed some pretty potent remedies. Her prescription for angina contained ox gall, pyrethrum, honey and pepper. Contemporary opinion was that it was 'almost strong enough to raise the dead.' Her husband, Mark Anthony, apparently found her physically unalluring whatever her intellectual rating was, as he left her in favour of Cleopatra. As the glorious blaze of the Greek and Roman Empires gradually burnt itself out women once again became prominent as doctors and medical aides. Men were preoccupied with fighting and religious dogma and the women folk rallied around caring for the sick.

Between the Middle Ages and the 16th century most of the medical women in Europe were women of the Church. These nuns and abbesses were of the practical type and their interests and activities were not necessarily confined to those of theology. Again as civilisation advanced, from the intellectual point of view, the ladies found themselves taking a back seat. Hannah Woolley, said to be 'good looking and skilled in physic and surgery,' was a typical example of what the 17th century expected of a woman medically. She wrote several books on medicine and cooking and was a sort of 17th-century Mrs Beeton. Her remedies are much nearer in spirit to Quackery than medicine. One for the 'Gravel' was the 'well-powdered roe of a red herring beaten to powder and taken in a glass of Rhine wine.' Another one, a pain cure, is rather difficult to understand. It involved lying in horse dung for eighteen days. With such ideas as these appearing in print it is understandable that men like Harvey, Sydenham, Willis and Chamberlen raised their eyebrows at the mention of the lady doctor.

If the girls were dragging their feet as far as orthodox medicine was concerned their sisters in arms, the lady Quacks were taking up the cudgels in this chapter of female franchisement. In the 17th century they usually described themselves as 'gentlewomen,' or occasionally as 'wife of the famous doctor now deceased.' Such a woman was Mary Green.

Mary lived in Chancery Lane and claimed to be licensed by His Grace the Lord Archbishop of Canterbury. Be this as it may she certainly seemed to know her stuff. She announced on her Handbills that she could cure 'All Deafness, Numbness, weakness of Limbs, Rheumatism and Sciaticas, though of many years standing,' and goes on to say that she 'has cured many who have

been advised amputation by eminent Physicians.' Two testimonials of Mary's are worth mentioning. 'Mr Robert Smith,
who two years ago was struck by a PLANET on his left arm, did
apply himself to the ablest physicians and surgeons in London,
and found no relief, but applying himself to the said Mrs Green
was in a short time perfectly cured by her and is now as well as
any man can be.'

A truly remarkable cure and no less impressive is the one that
she carried out on a Mrs Atkins, midwife of Scrupes Court, Holborn. She, unfortunate woman, was 'lame in all her limbs,' and
had apparently for four years consulted doctors and likewise 'the
whole College of Physicians' without relief, until she was fortunate enough to run across Mrs Green who 'perfectly cured her.'

Widow Drew was another bright girl at the game, advertising
herself as the daughter of a Doctor of Physics. After twenty years
or so of helping Father with his practise she took a short course
in midwifery from Doctor Rose, a prominent man midwife, to
'improve herself.' Suitably improved and confident she introduced her famous pills on to the market. These were to cure the
green sickness and change the 'pale, greenish tallow-coloured,
nasty and deathlike look on the patient into a lovely, florid and
healthy complexion.' She further claimed that 'many young
virgins have had the benefit of these pills,' which could be
obtained at the upper end of Gun Yard in Hounsditch.

Cures for the green sickness or chlorosis are mentioned in
many Quacks' pamphlets about this time. The disease itself was
something of a mystery to Doctors and Quacks alike. Dr R.
James, an eminent M.D. in 1745, described it as 'a disorder
which virgins fall into for want of their due menstrual discharge,'
and went on to say that 'if skilfully treated it is neither very
dangerous or of long duration. In virgins being happily cured
by marriage alone.' The Doctor's description is an interesting
one because we know now that he had got it absolutely back to
front. Chlorosis is an anaemic condition brought about by
inadequate diet and aggravated by lack of fresh air and exercise.
The menstrual disturbances are an attempt by the body to
conserve iron and are a result rather than the cause of the disease.
Chlorosis was probably the cause of 'swooning' so dear to the
authors of 18th- and 19th-century novels. Nowadays, probably
due to more sensible eating habits, chlorosis is a rare disease

and Widow Drew would have had little sale for her famous pills.

The 17th-century lady quack who called herself Agnodice had certainly read her classics. Her office at the 'Hand and Urinal' might have been better placed perhaps, particularly as her remedies were 'refined ones for gentlefolk.' She considered herself an expert on 'the diseases in particular I shall forbear to mention, they being not proper to expose to the public.' If the penny does not drop at this subtle innuendo she goes on, in a Handbill, to say that 'if Venus should misfortunately be wounded with Scorponious poison by tampering with fiery Mars . . . It is then she brings comfort and by her antidotes expels the poison Jovelike.'

Venereal disease was not the only social disease that Agnodice claimed to cure as she had a remedy for the Scotch disease. This was probably Scabies. Leaving diseases aside Agnodice was something of a beautician. Her Italian wash was advertised for skin blemishes. Her Spanish Rolls which seem to have been a 'pancake' type of make-up, useful for covering up pock marks, probably sold as easily as modern cosmetics do today. It is likely that it would have been made from the same simple basic ingredients, starch and talc.

Another anonymous gentlewoman who lived at the 'Surgeon's Sign' in the Haymarket also made cosmetics her chief concern. The psychology of her advertisement Handbill is interesting and is of a basic type still seen today. The message is, if you don't use A, B or C, then Miss D, E or F will probably steal your husband. To quote the Bill:

God, the author of all good things, to make man in love with his wife in her state of innocency, he made her smooth, soft, delicate and fair, to entice him to embrace her, I, therefore, that women might be pleasing to their husbands, and that they might not be offended at their deformities and turn into other women's chambers, do recommend unto you the virtue of an eminent and highly approved balsamick essence, with several incomparable cosmetics, faithfully prepared without mercury, price 1/–.

She also advertised depilatory ointment, available for a 1/–, and incredibly, 'a super-super-excellent paste for the shaking and trembling of the hands, after hard drinking or otherwise! – 1/– box.' Really! Ladies!

The last Quack from whose pamphlets we shall quote had the

makings in her of a modern Quack businesswoman in her specialisation in 'female disorders and weaknesses' of the more grisly kind. She was Ann Lavernerst, a German gentlewoman who was advertising herself, she explained, because 'otherwise for some years she might remain unknown.' She could cure, she modestly states, 'all women, or maids, of the suffocation, rising of the mother (womb) which may be occasioned through any rotten substance, or by stopping of their natural courses.' Also, 'outsinking, downfalling, or outhangings from the mother, that is when the ligaments and strings that bind the mother to the body, removes from its place, either by the bearing of children, violent coughing, heavy work . . .'

As if this is not enough practical gynaecology she also claimed she could cure 'women or maids that have not had their natural courses, likewise those who have had too many, also prevent loss of appetite, or unusual appetite that maids have for chalk, coals, etc.' Even the less inhibited of the copyrighters of the modern female pill advertisements would find it difficult to beat Ann at the game. It is doubtful if the various gentlewomen, whose Handbills are preserved in a collection in the British Museum, had much more than a fleeting fame although they probably made quite a comfortable living.

Two exceptions were Mrs Mapp, and Joanna Stephens. Mrs Sarah Mapp was a bone-setter. Today she might have been called a chiropractor or osteopath. Bone-setting and manipulative technique of many kinds have often been suspected as being unprofessional procedures. But there is a reputable side to this form of treatment. Manipulative orthopaedic surgery is now recognised as being a very successful as well as a very highly specialised subject.

Mrs Mapp's father was a Wiltshire bone-setter of no great moment and Sarah obviously learnt the tricks of the trade from him. After something of a family tiff she left home and started to tour the country calling herself 'Crazy Sally.' Her eccentricity, which was described by some as madness, was obviously part of her stock in trade. There was nothing crazy in her methods of business, however, for she chose Epsom as her centre of operations.

At this time (1736), Epsom was a watering place and a centre of fashionable and gay company. Sally was doing well, for the *London Magazine* gave her a gratuitous advertisement. It reported a 'young woman in Epsom who though not very regular, it is said, in her conduct, has wrought such cures as seem miraculous in the bone-setting way. The concourse of people on this occasion is incredible, and 'tis reckoned she get near 20 guineas a day.' This was not bad going in the days when coal was 22/– ton, French brandy was 6/– gallon and a good dinner at an inn might cost you 6d. Epsom was not slow to appreciate the value of such a popular medical figure to the community, and gave crazy Sally an honorarium of 300 guineas a year to secure her presence in the town.

All went well until love walked into Sally's life in the form of a footman known as Hill Mapp. His effect on our good bone-setter was so profound that she could not bring herself to do any more work until she was wed. The story of her wedding ride to London to marry her lover was well reported in typical 18th-century style in many contemporary magazines. Eventually the world breathed a sigh of relief when it heard that Mrs Mapp was back in business at Epsom. Alas for our heroine, the path of true love did not run smooth and the *Grub Street Journal* of the 19th April, 1736, states that 'we learn that the husband of Mrs Mapp, the famous bone-setter at Epsom, ran away from her last week, taking with him upwards of 100 guineas and such other portable things as lay next to his hand.' Several letters from Epsom mention that 'the footman, that the fair bone-setter married the week before, had taken a sudden journey from thence with what money his wife had earned, and that her concern was at first very great, but soon as the surprise was over she grew gay, and seems to think that money well disposed of as it was like to rid her of a husband.'

Far from upsetting her professional activities Mrs Mapp's desertion by her husband seems to have increased her standing and she was even consulted by the Queen. Sarah had taken to coming to London twice a week in her chariot drawn by four horses and held 'clinics' and met friends at the famous Grecian Coffee House. A play was written about her and she enjoyed hearing this song cheered by a large audience at the Playhouse in Lincoln's Inn Fields.

> 'You surgeons of London who puzzle your pates
> To ride in your coaches and purchase estates

Give over for shame for your pride has a fall
And ye doctress of Epsom has outdone you all.

Dame Nature has given her a doctor's degree
She gets all ye patients and pockets the fee
So if you don't instantly prove her a cheat
She'll loll in her chariot while you walk ye street.'

What can we make of this flamboyant person? She undoubtedly had great character. When her coach became stuck in one of London's muddy streets the crowd that gathered at first mistook her for a distinguished and unpopular gentlewoman. The mob, in truculent mood, advanced on her carriage. Mrs Mapp dispersed them with alacrity by shouting at them, 'Damn your bloods. Don't you know me? I'm Mrs Mapp the bone-setter!'

Physically she was repulsive. Cruikshank drew her with cross-eyes, set in a bloated, myxoedematous face. Her neck was short and set her head on enormous shoulders. Her hands, pudgy and powerful, were obviously good servants to her muscular arms. Her strength was enormous. She could set a dislocated shoulder unaided. She could put one 'out' just as easily. She demonstrated this when some local doctor sent her a bogus case to try to trick her. Mrs Mapp obviously believed in examining her patients thoroughly before treating them for she soon discovered the hoax. Her quick-witted if somewhat grim sense of humour is demonstrated nicely by the fact that she purposely dislocated the trickster's shoulder and sent him packing back to his sponsor. Her parting shot to this unfortunate was that he could get his own doctors to put his shoulder back! If they couldn't do it she said she would repair the damage herself in a month's time!

Professionally, within her limits she was obviously a clever operator. Contemporary records all speak of her quickness in manipulation. She chose her cases with discretion and did not pose as a cure-all. Apart from the practical work of setting fractured limbs and reducing dislocations, which she did with great skill, Mrs Mapp was one of the first manipulative specialists. In any community there are people experiencing pain or deformity due to various disabilities that will respond favourably to manipulation.

Such a person was the niece of Sir Hans Sloane. Sir Hans was an eminent medical man, the President of the College of

Physicians, and the first English Physician to be created a baronet. His famous collection of books, specimens and antiquities was eventually to become the nucleus of the British Museum. His niece had a spinal deformity and it is likely that she would have been treated by the most eminent doctors in London. The failure of orthodox medicine was apparent and Sloane called in Mrs Mapp who rapidly effected a cure. The august Baronet obviously approved of her skill and the good Sally performed many 'Miraculous cures' before him in the Grecian Coffee House.

It is easy to see how this must have enhanced her popular reputation and angered a large fraction of the medical profession. Percival Pott, a man whose name lives today in the description of two orthopaedic conditions (Pott's fracture, Pott's disease of the spine), did not share Sir Hans' favourable opinion of Mrs Mapp. He publicly deplored that 'people of all classes were believing the extravagant assertions of this ignorant, illiberal, drunken female savage,' and were even soliciting and enjoying her company. Mrs Mapp shared one thing with reputable doctors. She had her problem patients. For instance one Thomas Barber, a tallow chandler, invited 'any person affected with lameness to see the dressing of his leg' which was sound, he alleged, 'before Mrs Mapp's operation and to whom he now owed his unhappy confinement in a chair.' One is tempted to ask why, in such a sound condition, he went to the bone-setter at all?

Mrs Mapp's fate is somewhat obscure. Reading between the lines one gathers that some of her eccentricity was due to over-indulgence in gin. It may be that some of the 'blades' she met in the Grecian Coffee House led her into extravagant tastes and evil ways for she died penniless in her lodgings at Seven Dials, now Cambridge Circus, 'so poor that the parish were forced to bury her.' All in all, Sarah Mapp, despite her craziness and eccentricities seems to have been fairly honest. If she bamboozled a few fools and even made a few of her patients worse by her manipulations then to many others she brought relief and cure.

Joanna Stephens, who preceded Mrs Mapp by some forty years in her career of Quackery, probably cured no one except a few psychopaths. Her claim to fame is that she did not only fool her enthusiastic patients, but eventually the representatives of the whole British nation. Unfortunately we have no idea what Joanna looked like but in all probability her appearance is unimportant. Her personality and saleswomanship must have been prodigious. From the very beginning of her career she ingratiated herself with a large number of aristocrats and politicians. Joanna's speciality was the treatment of 'Stone.' Such was her cunning and persuasion that she not only impressed the rich with her cures but managed to convince a large number of scientists and physicians of their authenticity. Although Mrs Mapp had a few influential followers Joanna Stephens commanded the attention and respect of a large proportion of the influential thinkers of her day. For two or three years she rode upon the crest of the wave as far as popularity was concerned. An interesting facet in her personality is disclosed by the fact that at the moment when her reputation was at its highest she decided to make a *coup de grâce*.

In 1738 the *Gentleman's Magazine* joyously announced that Mrs Stephens had decided to disclose the secret of her remedy to the public for a consideration of a mere £5,000. Such were the times that this magnificent offer was hailed as a real act of benevolence on poor, suffering humanity. A public subscription was instantly launched and soon money began to roll in from such worthies as the Earl of Pembroke, the Duke of Richmond, the Bishops of Oxford and Gloucester and even Prime Minister Godolphin. When the subscription list closed, however, the sum was found to have reached only £1,365. Public opinion was so anxious that Mrs Stephens' fantastic cure should not be lost to posterity that eventually a Parliamentary Commission was duly appointed 'to enquire into the cures performed by Joanna Stephens.' The Commission duly sat and 'examined the said medicines and her method of preparing the same and found themselves convinced by experiment of the utility, efficiency and resolving power thereof.'

The members of the Commission were men of distinction and letters. Incredibly enough it included the famous William Cheseldon. He was an experimental surgeon of great perception and a pioneer operator for lithotomy (cutting for stone). His technique was original and successful and he became famous all over Europe. His reputation in London was so high that he was appointed consultant surgeon to the newly formed St George's hospital in 1734. One wonders why he lent his name to such a swindle. Cheseldon was not the only medical member of the

Commission. David Hartley was another physician and a philosopher very popular in his day (Coleridge thought so well of him that he named one of his sons after him). He published a book in which he examines the various cures of Mrs Stephens and comes out fair and square on the side of the Quack.

An account of the wonderful cure given in the *Gentleman's Magazine* in 1739, told the British public what value they had got for their £5,000. Joanna had three stock medicines. No. 1, a powder made of Calcined Eggshells and Snails. No. 2, a decoction of herbs, soap, honey and swines' cresses. No. 3, a pill consisting of snails, calcined, wild carrot seed, burdock seed, ashen keys, hips and haws (all burned to blackness – which would remove any alkaloid that might conceivably have a thera-peutic effect), soap and honey. One would have expected a public outcry to have occurred when the formula of the cure was dis-closed, but there is no evidence that there was any such thing. Admittedly there were some voices crying in the wilderness. One such voice was that of Benjamin Franklin who was visiting England at this time. Although he was at first impressed with the cures that had been claimed for the famous pills he came to the conclusion that 'their contents must become changed during the passage from the stomach to the bladder and that nothing possibly dissolves stones at that distance.'

And yet people used the recipe, and others like it, for many years to come. Sir Robert Walpole who died in 1745, a man who bestrode his generation like a Colossus, would have been a difficult man to hoodwink. He was a victim of the stone and it has been calculated that during his last years he consumed some 180 lb. of soap in the hope of alleviating his symptoms. After his death a postmortem was carried out and three large stones were found in his bladder, monuments to the power of Quackery.

The ultimate fate of Joanna and her £5,000 does not appear to be known. It would be nice to think that she fled to America, bequeathing her genetic characteristics to a family of New Englanders that lived around Boston. In the year 1819 a woman was born whom Joanna would have admired. Her name was Lydia Estes who eventually became Lydia Pinkham. Mrs Pink-ham has been described as America's first successful business woman. She was also perhaps the first millionairess. The Com-pany that she and her family founded were pioneers in the field of advertising and if the famous Vegetable Compound that she invented, on closer examination seems to be rather bogus, the Pinkham business methods were A.1. Lydia Pinkham has been considered interesting enough as a person to attract biographers and there is no dearth of material about her.

As a young woman she was a free thinker and some of her escapades would cause eyebrows to be raised even today. New England in the 1840's was a conventional place, but Lydia had been brought up to be a rather unconventional young woman. She was an ardent supporter of women's rights and temperance. She was also very much against, a subject still in the news, the colour bar. She organised a debating society at Lynn, where she was a local schoolmistress. The wording of the constitution of the society is highly significant and shows us just what was going on in Lydia's mind in those early days. It ran: 'no person shall be excluded from full participation in any of the operations of this society on account of sex, complexion or religious or political opinions.' While the members were debating such world shattering questions as 'would it be a beneficial arrangement to the community to have those clergymen who advocate judicial murder appointed state hangmen?' there is evidence that young Lydia was not always preoccupied with thoughts of reform and suffrage. She fell in love with a fellow debater, Isaac Pinkham, when she was 24 and married him within a few months.

Isaac, described as a dapper, polite man of great charm had a good background and was probably the sort of man who would appeal to a strong-minded young woman like Lydia. The fact that he was a widower with one child by his first wife made him more attractive to someone who was devoting so much of her time to lost causes and unpopular reforms. The evidence, such as it is, tends to support the assumption that Lydia and Isaac were happy enough and settled in a house in Lynn, bought for them by Lydia's father. Here they raised a family of three sons and a daughter.

Whatever Isaac was like as a father we do not know. That he was completely useless as a business man is quite certain. Everything he touched seemed to go wrong. Between 1843 and 1873 he must have been the only Real Estate man not to make a fortune, and when his last financial gamble failed he was, at sixty, a broken man who had finally lost faith in everything, including himself. The Pinkhams had to sell up and go and live in a cottage, lick their wounds and decide on a course of action. Apart from father, the family was in good shape. The boys had all had a high school education and without fail had headed the class and obtained all the prizes available. In true American fashion, they worked in their spare time and learned the value of money. Lydia never had enough spare money to take things easily at home and probably developed into a fairly tough and managing middle-aged woman. At fifty-four she was still a person with very definite ideas about things. She knew what she liked and what she did not. One of the things she liked was herbal remedies. One of the things she definitely disliked was Doctors.

In those days there was quite a lot to be said for her opinion. Mid-19th-century America was not noted for its medical men. Many 'private' medical schools existed, side by side with a few reputable ones. These private schools specialised in turning out doctors quickly and economically. Unfortunately, Medicine is an art based on observation, thought, and experience. It is unlikely that men who were 'graduating' as doctors after only one term of lectures would come up to Mrs Pinkham's or anybody else's standards. And so 'to doctor' meant, contemporarily, 'to bungle.'

If general medicine was bad in Lynn, Massachusetts, gynae-cology and midwifery were worse. Women were expected to die in childbirth as a matter of course. Puerperal fever was rife. Side by side with excessive female modesty, there was much sexual promiscuity and venereal disease. In 1890 a writer on the history of prostitution gave the amazing news that in New York City it was estimated that there was one prostitute for every fifty-five inhabitants. Child prostitution was common. A consultant surgeon to the City Hospital of New York wrote of a child of fourteen living in a tenement in New York who had given venereal disease to eleven others living under the same roof. In what must have been the understatement of the year he is quoted as saying, 'this would seem to suggest that there was an *almost* promiscuous intercourse among the occupants of the building.'

One of the few gynaecologists of the day was quoted as saying:

The relations between the sexes are of so delicate a character that the duties of the medical practitioner are necessarily more difficult when he comes to take charge of a patient labouring under one of the great host of female complaints . . . I confess that I am bound to say that there are women who prefer to suffer the extremity of danger and pain, rather than waive the scruples of delicacy which prevent their maladies being fully explored . . . Nevertheless a greater candour on the part of the patient would scarcely fail to bring to light in their early stages curable maladies.

He goes on to illustrate his point by quoting a case. A woman who had previously been treated by several doctors for painful periods had told him that not one doctor had thought it necessary to examine the womb by means of a speculum. With medicine in this sort of quandary things were just right for the Quacks. As doctors were unreliable most women with 'female complaints' favoured self treatment with a suitable remedy.

Mrs Pinkham had such a remedy and had been using it for some time on friends and relatives. To date there had been no question of selling it we are told. But things in the Pinkham household had for a long time been going from bad to worse. Although the boys were through school, money was tight and good jobs were hard to come by. And so one day, when a stranger arrived at the door wanting a bottle of Mrs Pinkham's remedy so badly that he was prepared to pay hard cash for it, an idea was born and the Pinkhams were in business.

The origin of the recipe for what was to become famous as Pinkham's Vegetable Compound is surrounded in conjecture. Some think that a debtor of Isaac's (not a rare bird, as one of Isaac's business failings was boundless generosity), gave the recipe to the family instead of the repayment of a loan. More likely is the tale that Mrs Pinkham, always keen on herbal remedies, found it in her copy of the *American Dispensary*, a massive know-all of botanical recipes popular in her day. Anyway, as soon as the Pinkhams realised that a market was there, they explored it energetically.

Lydia E. Pinkham's Vegetable Compound was launched. Lydia scrubbed out the cellar and got down to brewing the remedy in larger quantities than she had ever dreamed of. The whole family turned to in the evening for bottling while poor Isaac was prevailed upon to read aloud to break the monotony. When they were not wanted for manufacturing chores the boys were sent out into the surrounding neighbourhood to push hand-bills through the letter-boxes of Lynn and Boston.

The copy for the handbills was composed by Lydia herself originally, as were the labels on the bottles. She was also working on a modest booklet of some four pages entitled *A Guide to Women*. Her style was admirable, quackwise. She had an obvious flair for writing and her advice was comforting and dogmatic. The guide was to become quite a classic. In 1901 it had grown to a sixty-two page book in five languages.

But this is jumping ahead too far. The early days of the Compound's history were fraught with anxiety. After a few years local markets for the Compound were increasing and Mrs Pinkham's three boys began to think of giving up their regular jobs and devoting their whole time to the family business. Dan, the eldest one, was the first to take the plunge. The family had decided that if they were ever to do big business then they must expand. As a result of this Dan departed for New York in the spring of 1876 with a stack of handbills and a barrel of medicine to conquer the city.

He worked like a slave, never sparing himself in his efforts to promote sales of the Compound in every possible way. Even when orders were looking up he was still insisting in laying out money in further advertisements for sales promotion. Eventually he hit on the then original idea of newspaper advertising, complete with a picture of Lydia. This proved to be an enormous success. Mrs Pinkham's face, 'so full of character and sympathy,' approximated to the nation's idea of everybody's old mother. Here was somebody who could cure female complaints if anybody could! As Mrs Pinkham's comforting and homely face became more widely known sales boomed and by 1881 it was estimated that they were grossing 30,000 dollars a month. Here was the first sweet taste of success. It was also the family's first taste of personal tragedy, for in the autumn of the same year Dan died, aged 33 years.

For some time it had been obvious that he had contracted tuberculosis. The long, breakneck months in New York had taken their toll. Unfortunately, Will, the youngest son, must have caught the disease from Dan for in two months he was dead also, at the age of 28. His young wife died of the disease some months later. When Lydia herself died in 1883 the end of an era was reached in the history of the business, now a registered company, Lydia Pinkham, Sons & Company. Over the years it had prospered tremendously and pioneered many of the accepted principles of modern advertising technique.

What will be history's verdict on Lydia Pinkham? Lydia's biographers have tended to whitewash her and have given us the mental picture of a nice, intelligent woman, pushed into business by adversity and into the public eye because she was a good herbalist. We are asked to believe that Lydia herself thought her Compound was a boon to humanity in days when doctors were unreliable.

This picture is far from true. There is ample evidence that the Pinkhams knew what nonsense the Compound really was. Dan's letters home are enlightening on this subject. Soon after his arrival in New York he is asking for a keg of Compound to be sent to him to give away as free samples. He says with admirable candour, 'We can't lose much and I think it will be a grand thing as it would get these millinery storekeepers and dressmakers guzzling it.' There is nothing about suffering humanity here. Later, when he was rather depressed that female complaints were not quite the money spinners that he had thought, he advised the family to include male complaints and their cure in the pamphlets. Writing home, he says, 'I think there is one thing we are missing out on, that is not having something in the pamphlets with regard to kidney complaints, as about half the people out here are troubled with kidney complaints or think they are.'

The family's religious feelings were not particularly squeamish. Again Dan writes about trying out a new magazine for the Compound's advertisement. He advises the family to run a small advertisement in 'a religious little paper that nobody but women would read.' This would, he thought, 'give a kind of religious tone to our Compound and get the goodwill of a few Methodists for it.' Dan's letters, directed, as we are told by Jean Burton, Mrs Pinkham's very competent biographer, to the whole family, must reflect what was the real Pinkham attitude to the Compound.

Lydia, as we have seen, wrote most of the copy and designed the labels. A label in use when she was alive and presumably written by her, tells us that Lydia Pinkham's Vegetable Compound is a sure cure for Prolapsus Uteri or Falling of the Womb. Lydia Pinkham must have known that the condition of Prolapsed Uterus, caused as it is by the mechanics of the pelvis being

disturbed structurally, perhaps by childbirth, could not be cured
by medicine. The best that could be hoped for was that the
symptoms of prolapse would perhaps be blunted to some extent
by the alcohol content of the Compound. It was also alleged on
the label that it would cure 'all female weaknesses including
leucorrhoea, irregular and painful menstruation, inflammation
and ulceration of the womb, flooding, etc.' Small print tells us
that the Compound is 'pleasant to the taste, efficacious and
immediate in its effects. It is a great help in pregnancy and
relieves pain during labour.' Perhaps an aphrodisiac effect is
hinted at in the claim that 'it is for all weaknesses of the
generative organs of either sex.'

Dan's advice is reflected in the statement that, 'it is second
to no remedy that has ever been before the public for all diseases
of the kidney.' With characteristic modesty the label concludes
that the Compound is 'the greatest remedy in the world.' This
would hardly seem to be in the style of a genteel and motherly
figure who felt quite genuinely that she had something for
suffering humanity. It is much more akin, surely, to the confident
traditions of Quackery. Mrs Pinkham changed the material of
her advertising to suit the occasion. For instance, when Dan
stood (successfully) for the Lower House of the State Legisla-
ture, she wove a political handout into her current pamphlets.

A startling item of news was unlikely to be overlooked if it
provided useful capital for the Compound. 'Fearful Tragedy, a
Clergyman of Stratford, Connecticut, killed by his own wife,
insanity brought on from sixteen years suffering of female
complaints the cause. Lydia E. Pinkham's Vegetable Compound,
the sure cure for these complaints would have prevented the
dreadful deed.' This is also rather a difficult pill to swallow if we
are to believe the benign old grey-haired grandmother myth
which had been woven round the name of Lydia E. Pinkham.

As has been previously suggested the therapeutic effect, if
any, of the Compound was in all probability due to its alcohol
content. Originally the mixture contained 18 per cent alcohol. In
other words two bottles of the Compound were equivalent to
one bottle of whisky. Alcohol is a good, and was probably the
very first tranquilliser. Unfortunately, its effects are quickly
limited by tolerance. It is also a drug of addiction as Lydia well
knew. It is really incredible that an erstwhile abolitionist could

countenance a frankly alcoholic beverage. And yet we hear that as far as alcohol was concerned, Mrs Pinkham was merely against social drinking. In sickness, whisky, sherry or, preferably, the Compound, were all important medicines.

This strong streak of hypocrisy seems to have been a Pinkham trait. It is well demonstrated in the family's treatment of Dan Pinkham when he was doing his pioneer pamphlet spreading in New York City. Dan was often in desperate straits in those days as is shown by his letters home. For example, 'just received your letter of the 20th and found no money in it. Now, for God's sake how do you expect me to live here in Brooklyn without sending me any money.' He goes on to enumerate his modest expenses and tells how he is sewing up his shoes so that he can keep on the road. In a later letter he 'cusses the judgement that sends him only five dollars,' and says that due to this he will 'have to loaf tomorrow and live on a cracker diet.' To conclude he complains, 'by the time you receive this letter my appetite will be good enough to hanker after a good, square meal.' During this time Dan was working extremely hard by all accounts, and overwork and poor food probably did a lot towards lowering his previously robust constitution, making him an easy prey to the tuberculosis that was shortly to kill him. It seems odd that the benign lady of Lynn should turn a deaf ear to the pleas of her eldest son, especially when business at home was beginning to pick up. And yet she did.

This rather tricky attitude to life in general is seen in the Pinkham Company's advertising in later years. Lydia herself had built up a personal advice gimmick. In her advertisements women were invited to write to Lydia Pinkham about their female problems. At first she answered all the letters herself, but as time went by and the volume of correspondence increased, she was forced to employ assistants to do this work. This would be fair enough as long as the firm no longer implied that Lydia E. Pinkham was replying personally to all enquiries. Samuel Hopkins Adams, a great debunker of patent medicines wrote in Collier's Magazine:

No little stress is laid on personal advice by the patent medicine companies. This may be, according to the statements of the firm, from their physician or from some special expert. As a matter of fact it is almost invariably furnished by a 10-dollar-a-week typist, following out one of a number of form letters prepared in bulk for the personal enquiry dupes. Such is the Lydia E. Pinkham method. The Pinkham company writes me that it is entirely innocent of any intention to deceive people into believing that Lydia E. Pinkham is still alive, and that it has published in several cases statements regarding her demise. It is true that a number of years ago a newspaper forced the Pinkham concern into a defensive admission of Lydia E. Pinkham's death, but since then the main purpose of the Pinkham advertising has been to fool the feminine public into believing that their letters go to a woman – who died nearly twenty years ago of one of the diseases, it is said, which her remedy claims to cure. True, the newspaper appeal is always, 'write to Mrs Pinkham,' and this is technically a saving clause as there is a Mrs Pinkham, the widow of the son of Lydia E. Pinkham. What sense of shame she might be supposed to suffer in the perpetration of an obvious and public fraud is presumably salved by the large profits of the business. The great majority of the gulls who write to Mrs Pinkham suppose themselves to be addressing Lydia E. Pinkham, and their letters are not even answered by the present proprietor of the name, but by a score of hired clerks and typists.

Since the early days the Vegetable Compound has undergone many changes. The product sold today is a thoroughly respectable herbal remedy. It also has an oestrogen content. Regular doses would therefore be beneficial to women in the menopause, although few physicians would consider self-medication with oestrogens a desirable practice.

Students and doctors on both sides of the Atlantic have been heard to sing after medical conferences or dinners, various versions of the Lydia Pinkham song. The popular British one is:

'And so we drink, we drink, we drink to Lydia Pink,
Saviour of the human race,
She invented the Vegetable Compound,
Efficacious in every case.'

The sarcasm here is obvious. The Medical Profession has for a long time held the view that Lydia E. Pinkham was not the saviour she is supposed to have been. Perhaps she would have been a more likeable character if she had not hidden behind a reputation of New England learning and gentility. Yet if she had come out into the open to quack loudly like the others her fate might have been very different. With a few exceptions her sister Quacks all died in obscurity. Lydia Pinkham died a very rich woman and the Company she formed made millions.

10

ODD CURES

1. *The Natural History of Teething Rings*

It is difficult to understand the success of some Quack Remedies, but teething and toothache cures do not come into this category. From the very beginning they were winners, and some of the earliest Quacks made them their speciality.

During the 15th century a cure was not thought to be up to much unless it had a Saint's name attached to it. St Apollonia was the most popular patron of toothache therapy. The teeth of the Saint, believed to be a certain preventive against tooth-ache, were much sought after. King Henry VI, a naturally religious man, became so appalled at this medieval com-mercialisation that he ordered anyone possessing these relics to hand them over to his agents. It was reported by Fuller, the church historian, that, 'a ton of veritable teeth of St Apollonia were thus collected together, and were her stomach proportionate to her teeth, a country could scarce afford her a meal.'

The bones of Saints were also very popular as teething rings. St Hugh's bones were thought to be particularly efficacious. There is an interesting little story of how this belief came about. St Hugh was a great lover of children, and when they were having teething troubles he 'dipped his finger in holy water and so, going gently over their gums nine times, upon removing his said finger the last time, out popped the tooth.' St Hugh's reputation was so high as far as children were concerned that an unscrupulous monk took advantage of it in the following way. 'A young lady, who, having been married a long time to an ancient knight without children,' asked her confessor for advice.

One evening while sitting alone in her garden, the priest, representing himself to be St Hugh approached her and told her that he knew of her troubles. 'St Hugh' recommended a course of action of no great originality and the aged knight's deficiency was made good 'in the chapel the same evening, vespers being over.'

When the baby was born it became very ill with its teeth and was thought to be near death. Unfortunately, the wicked priest, already perhaps being punished for his foul deed, was dead. But the 'lady had a dream that if she could get one of 'St Hugh's' toes and rub the child's gums, it would recover. By bribing the sexton, the coffin was opened and the bone was brought. No sooner was the same applied but up starts two swanking teeth, the infant presently smiles and grew well.' From that day to this teething rings have been popular and 'anodyne necklaces,' a constant stock in trade for many Quacks.

An example of such an article was the one sold by Dr Chamberlen in the 1720's. From his house at Temple Bar he did a roaring trade and recommended his products to the world. 'A great number of children at death's door,' he assured the public, received 'ease and benefit' from his 'anodyne necklace' and the 'Liquid Coral' gum balm that went with it. A mere 5/– was all that was asked for these life-saving articles. He also offered wholesale facilities at '48/– a dozen sealed up to sell again,' and suggested that the anodyne necklaces would make suitable christening gifts for children.

As might be expected, some Quacks specialised in Dentistry. One 17th-century operator, David Perronet, invented a 'universal dentifrice' that makes our present day toothpaste advertisements appear pretty feeble. It made 'black teeth as ivory,' and was a 'sure and speedy remedy for the worst teeth-aches and such as be hollow or rotten: for be they never so long continued, this remedy will presently cure it by killing the worm in it.' Another colleague who lived nearby in the old City of London, Edward Comport, advertised that he 'letteth blood and draweth teeth dexterously and also cutteth issues for sixpence.'

Undoubtedly the most colourful of all Dental Quacks was Martin van Butchell. He practised in the 1770's and made 'real or artificial teeth from one to an entire set, with superlative gold pivots and springs : also gums, sockets and palate, formed, fitted, finished and fixed, without drawing stumps or causing pain.' With such a repertoire one would have thought van Butchell needed no further advertisement. But this was the Golden Age of English Quackery and competition ran high. To make sure he was seen, van Butchell travelled around London on a white pony, painted with purple spots. This probably made him distinctly noticeable, but he obtained more fame in a curious way. When his wife died, he got William Hunter to embalm her and fix her up in a display cabinet in his sitting-room.

Carmine dye injected into the blood vessels, and nicely matched glass eyes, made the lady quite lifelike. She became a permanent fixture about the house. Dressed in a 'fine lace gown,' she was always introduced by van Butchell as his 'dear departed,' and the Quack was said to have enjoyed a period of domestic tranquillity never previously experienced. Eventually, van Butchell felt he needed something more in the way of feminine company than a woman in a glass case, and remarried. His new wife, not unnaturally, objected to her predecessor's constant presence, and had the 'dear departed' removed to the College of Surgeons' Museum. There she remained for over 150 years in the company of another embalmed lady, the mistress of the 18th-century surgeon, John Sheldon, until one dark night in 1941, when a German bomb reduced them finally to ashes.

Before leaving the Natural History of Teething Rings, tooth pulling as an advertisement to General Quackery deserves special mention. Incredible as it may seem, many Quacks found they could raise a crowd easily by means of a few demonstrations of dentistry before the more serious business of the day commenced. A typical example of this device is seen in the activities of a Quack who practised in Paris in the early days of the 18th century.

His name was Le Grand Thomas, and his pitch was on the Pont Neuf. He must have been an impressive figure in his scarlet suit laced with gold. He wore on his head a large three-cornered hat trimmed with peacock's feathers, and at his side rattled a gigantic sabre. An immense man, it is said that he 'ate as four, drank in the same proportions, and slept eighteen hours out of twenty-four.' Although Grand Thomas sold a good

Quack nostrum that 'cured radically and surely the most secret diseases, without need to keep the patient in bed and also without friction or salivation,' he found it advantageous to do a little dentistry as an advertisement. The operations took place on an elegantly decorated cart that served for a stage. A huge 'crowned tooth' hung from the roof as a sort of trade mark. Here he 'extracted teeth without pain, maybe, but not without unfolding of strength.' Nearly two hundred years later similar displays were still going on in England.

Perhaps the most notorious exploiters in this field of Quackery were the manufacturers of 'Sequar's Oil' and 'Prairy Flower Mixture.' These two products were said to hail from the 'mineral springs in North America,' and to have been invented by the Sioux, Cherokee and Apache Indians. Such a background impressed prospective customers in the early 1900's, although it was disclosed by analytical spoilsports that 'Sequar's Oil' was only turpentine and fish oil, and the 'Prairy Flower' medicine, a mere mixture of bicarbonate of soda and aloes.

Sequar sold not on its formula, but by its presentation. The manufacturers had a fleet of highly decorated circus cars that toured large towns during the day carrying a brass band on top that played popular melodies. In the evening the cars were parked in widely advertised public places and a 'Dental Clinic' was held. As soon as a suitable crowd had arrived, 'Professor Sequar,' usually an Indian or a Negro, would draw up in a two-horse landau. Bouquets of flowers and baskets of fruit, presumably from grateful patients, were immediately presented to him. The Quack was eventually persuaded to take his place on the stand. Wearing a broad brimmed sombrero as part of an elaborate 'Western' outfit, he read aloud letters 'just handed to him.' These, of course, were fake testimonials.

After this, the 'Professor' fixed a small lamp onto his hat and retired into a cabin at the back of the car, to start extractions. The band struck up loudly playing the old spiritual, 'Who's dat callin' so sweet,' to drown the cries of the sufferers and the occasional crack of a tooth being broken during the operation. Once this 'fun' was over the 'Professor,' slightly bloodstained and not a little heated from his extractions, returned to his former place on the coach and sold the celebrated Sequar nostrums.

There is still a 'Professor Sequar' operating in England. He has moved as far away from his atavistic speciality as is possible, and sells ointment and powder to cure corns and callouses. Judging by the amount of money he was seen to take in an hour in Portsmouth market recently he is not doing too badly.

2. *Cool Clear Water*

Water, as a therapeutic substance, has many distinct advantages. It is cheap and clean, and can be used internally or externally. Water treatments of various kinds have been popular since Greco-Roman times. But classical conceptions of elegant bathing fell into disrepute in the Middle Ages and many 15th-century manuscripts give interesting evidence of the high jinks that went on in public baths.

Men and women, completely naked apart from their hats and jewellery, dined in baths together, off floating tables, while musicians played for those whose thoughts were not concerned with eating or drinking. As one contemporary observer wrote, 'men and women, maids and youths, monks and nuns, bathing together, quite naked, could certainly not promote chastity.' Later, when syphilis first broke out in Europe as an epidemic disease, public bathing was prohibited as it was thought to be spreading the infection.

Whether or not the age of Spa therapy, when every town of any size in Europe had its own special Spa or Hydro, followed on as an extension of these old practices, is debatable. There is no doubt that some of the Spas were centres of fashionable society. Social life and gambling were part and parcel of early Hydrotherapy. If the tastes of those partaking of water cures changed from voyeurism to Faro it need not bother us much.

Spa treatment was obviously a good thing for many of its devotees, as it gave them an excellent opportunity for a little exercise and the chance of an occasional wash, two items often neglected in that day and age. With the new vogue, as might be expected, came a good crop of Quacks. One of these was Vincent Priessnitz. He practised at Graefenberg in quite a big way. His clinic took 500 patients at a time and his clients were treated to a variety of procedures which became known as Hydropathy. Broadly, this consisted of hot and cold baths, sheets or wraps, a plain diet and the drinking of massive quantities of cold water.

Priessnitz could hardly be described as a fashionable figure. He was, we are told, 'built with broad shoulders without any tendency to fat, five feet eight inches in height, with an excellent phrenological development: having had his front teeth knocked out, appearing a larger man at a distance than he is found to be when you are closer, having a suspicious look: of few words, and drinking but milk at his breakfast and supper.'

Even with these disabilities, Priessnitz did well. He disciplined his patients strictly. They spent their days sawing wood or walking when they were not 'taking the waters,' either externally or internally. The plain diet they endured was probably strange to their tastes as it consisted only of soup, veal, mutton, pork and potatoes. On these slender premises the Hydropathist established a reputation, and eventually produced several disciples.

One of these, a Dr Wilson, later became physician to His Highness, the Prince of Nassau. During his apprenticeship to Priessnitz he underwent 500 cold baths, 2,400 Sitz baths, and spent 480 hours in wet sheets, drinking some 3,500 tumblers of cold water. It might be argued that he earned his place in the speciality.

Hydropathy was not limited to Continental Europe. A noted exponent in England was Dr Edward Johnson of Malvern. He decried 'drug practitioners' as 'doctors who dropped drugs of which they knew little into stomachs of which they knew less.' Reading his book, the *Domestic Practice of Hydropathy*, which ran into several editions in the 1850's, it is obvious that he had a large and successful practice. His method was precise and systematic. He divided Hydropathy into seventy-four rigid treatments. Number one was 'a shallow bath, immediately succeeded by a plunge, immediately succeeded by a shallow bath, each of the baths to last about a minute. The list proceeds through such exciting moments as number fourteen, 'wet friction – dry friction – wet friction – dry friction – wet friction – dry friction' – to end with a rather prosaic number seventy-four 'wash down with hot water, yellow soap and flannel.'

One of the seventy-four treatments cured, according to Dr Johnson, anything from Asthma to Apoplexy.

How did Hydropathy work? Here we are lucky for we have the doctor's own theory of this almost mystical science. 'I have shown,' he alleged, 'that the pores of the skin joined end to end would form a tube twenty-eight miles in length. Surely there can be no difficulty in believing that if this tube be obstructed and the matters which is intended to carry out of the blood be left in, while the matters which it is intended to convey into the blood be kept out of it, surely I can say, there can be no difficulty in believing that a very unhealthy and wrong state of the blood must be the necessary result. How plain and commonsense all this appears! How rational!' If today we find this 'commonsense' reasoning a little difficult to follow, it is unfortunate.

Hydropathy had a short vogue, although medicated baths are still sometimes used. As for the famous Spa waters of Malvern and Vichy, their erstwhile devotees would be horrified to see the use they are put to today. The chief call for these once much thought of therapeutic substances is now made not in the Hydro but at the Saloon Bar.

3. Under the Influence

The natural alliance between medicine and magnets was noted in a previous chapter. It all started with Paracelsus. He was a 16th-century physician whose revolutionary teaching labelled him a Quack in the eyes of his contemporaries. It did not help matters that he made a practice of burning copies of Galen's and Avicenna's works, then standard 'text books,' before he lectured his students. He told them to forget the old classical Medicine and follow his doctrines. One of Paracelsus's bright ideas was magnetic treatment. In a style reminiscent of Mrs Beeton, Paracelsus expounded, 'take a magnet impregnated with Mummy.' Paracelsus was strong on Mummys as well as magnets and detailed six kinds for everyday use. The best type of Mummy was made from criminals that had been hanged, as from these there was a 'gentle siccation that expungeth the watery humour, without destroying the oil and spiritual which is cherished by the heavenly luminaries and strengthened continually by the affluence of the impulses of the celestial spirits.'

Having taken the 'mummified' magnet he directed his followers to 'sow some seeds that have a congruity with disease.' The details of his technique then became rather complicated, but essentially it consisted of stroking the patient with the magnet and then thrusting the latter into the earth. As the seeds germinated and grew the patient's disease would diminish and finally be cured.

The ideas of Paracelsus were not all as stupid as this. For example, he stated that 'he who wants to look at a man must look upon him as a whole and not as a patched-up piece of work. If he finds a part of the body diseased he must look for causes that produce the disease.' If Paracelsus found the causes mystical, rather than physical, all well and good, but at least he did not subscribe to the 'dose and draught' medical philosophy so popular in his day.

A man born some two hundred years after these strange philosophies had been proposed gave his name to a medical cult that exists today. Franz Anton Mesmer was probably influenced by Paracelsus's doctrines. After studying religion, law and philosophy in Bavarian universities, he graduated in 1765. The following year, when he was thirty-two, he read the thesis which contained the germ of an idea that was to rule his life. It was entitled '*Disputatio de Planetarum Influxu*' and postulated that the stars and the planets not only influenced physical things such as tides and the hours of lightness, but also the human body. This effect was brought about, Mesmer maintained, by changes that were wrought on an invisible substance, the 'fluidum' that pervaded the whole body.

This thesis must have caused many eyebrows to be raised in the University of Vienna, although through it he obtained his M.D. Mesmer was, at this time, a hard working and conscientious doctor and had a well-run and properly conducted practice in the capital. He entered into a financially satisfactory marriage. He was greatly interested in music and through a friendship with Leopold Mozart was instumental in launching young Wolfgang Mozart on his musical career. His wife's wealth gave him ample funds with which to develop an experimental laboratory in his house where he continued his scientific studies. In 1774 he heard that a man, with a particularly ominous sounding name, Professor Maximillian Hell of the University of Vienna was curing people with magnets. After meeting Hell, Mesmer was sure that his 'fluidum' might have something to do with magnetism and electricity. Later he discovered he was able to cure patients as easily with magnets as Hell could.

In the early days it seems that Mesmer was quite sincere in his studies. He was subsequently convinced that magnets as such were only incidental to treatment and that his real power came from within. He believed that he could magnetise anything, paper, bread, silk, wood, dogs, men and finally, in a burst of megalomania, the sun itself. The success of Mesmer's treatments on psychosomatic patients was immense, and startling. It soon became an embarrassment and a worry to his professional colleagues. Eventually after a particularly unfortunate case, the University of Vienna appointed a Commission to investigate Mesmer's cures. The findings of this, admittedly much prejudiced body, were that he should stop 'his fraudulent practice,' or leave Vienna.

If Mesmer's career had stopped here there would have been little to say about him quackwise. The evidence seems to show that until this he was a sincere and conscientious man who had found out by accident the beginnings of the principles of hypnosis. On his expulsion from Vienna a change took place in Mesmer. Gone were the ideas of a disinterested scientist. Perhaps he felt that having been labelled a charlatan he would make the best of it.

He emigrated to Paris. The city in 1778 could hardly have been in a better state to receive him. Religion was outmoded, Voltaire was alive, and the medical profession was in the doldrums. Christoph Gluck, whom he had known in Vienna, was a favourite in Marie-Antoinette's Court. Soon things started to move. Mesmer published his *Memoir on the discovery of Animal Magnetism* and postulated his twenty-seven 'Propositions' on the subject. These explained the principles of Animal Magnetism in theory but the public were anxious to see them demonstrated. They had not long to wait for Mesmer opened his famous clinic at the Hotel Bullion in the Rue Montmartre.

The Clinic was sumptuous. Its floors were beautifully carpeted to deaden the tread and conversation was forbidden in the Salon. The only noise to be heard was gentle music which Mesmer found conducive to his treatment. Incense was burned and scent wafted through the lavishly furnished building. The walls of the Salon were almost covered with mirrors that had the effect of everybody being able to see what was happening all over the room, an important factor to some of Mesmer's patients as we shall see.

In the centre of the Salon was the Baquet. This was an oval vessel that contained bottles of 'magnetised water,' and was partially filled with water into which 'magnetised' iron filings were thrown. The Baquet was covered with a metal top through which projected long movable iron rods. These could be adjusted to be placed on the patients as required. Around this strange apparatus sat Mesmer's clientele, holding hands and pressing their knees together to form a magnetic circle. One can imagine the nervous tension rising in the susceptible and quite other feelings being experienced in the sexually repressed after a short period of this group therapy. Soon the assistant Magnetisers arrived. These, a contemporary observer tells us were, 'strong handsome young men who embraced the patients between the knees, rubbed them gently down the spine and the course of their necks, and used gentle pressure on the breasts of the ladies.'

With this sort of chicanery going on it is no wonder that, 'gradually the cheeks of the ladies began to glow, their imaginations became influenced and off they went one after the other, in convulsive fits. Some sobbed and tore their hair, others laughed until the tears ran from their eyes, while still others shrieked and screamed until they became insensible.'

This is a description of the 'Crisis' that Mesmer thought was so necessary for successful treatments.

As the 'Crisis' approached the Master attended the patients personally. At this time he dressed in a long, lilac coloured, embroidered silk robe and carried a white iron wand. He 'stroked the insensible with his hands upon their eyebrows and down the spine and traced figures on their breasts and abdomens – and then they were returned to consciousness.' If the 'Crises' were particularly violent, patients were removed to a special

room elaborately padded with pink silk and were restrained
until their nervous energy was exhausted.

Clearly Mesmer was now practising frank Quackery. He was
making a small fortune and cunningly exploiting the foibles of
his time. It was said that he offered everyone a bribe, 'to the
afflicted he offered help, to the victim of ennui, a new sensation:
to the scientific smatterer, a pretty psychological puzzle: to the
intriguing butterfly of fashion, a pastime; and to the debauchée
the sensual gratification of watching the convulsive and un-
restrained movements of lovely women.'

Strange as it may seem even at this stage Mesmer hankered
after official recognition. The fact that the Queen enthused over
his practices and Madame du Barry had a magnetic apparatus
set up at Louveciennes, was not enough for him. Eventually,
Louis XVI was persuaded to appoint a Commission to investigate Animal Magnetism. Its members were men of fame
and distinction and included Benjamin Franklin, Lavoisier, Jean
Sylvain Bailly, and Dr Guillotin, whose name will be possibly
remembered more than any of them. The investigations of the
Commissioners were extensive and fairly exhaustive. Their
judgement is summed up with typical French economy, as
'*L'imagination fait tout, le magnétisme nul.*' This unfortunate
decision did not do much to lessen Mesmer's popularity which
continued until the fatal year of 1792. Then many heads, including those of Commissioners Bailly and Lavoisier fell into
the basket that stood in front of the terrible machine that also
killed with a kind of mechanical patricide, its own inventor.

These early signs of *La Terreur* that was to follow, made
Mesmer flee to Germany, but he returned to Paris some six
years later. It is a credit to his powers of tenacity and persuasion
that he obtained from the new Government a pension of 3,000
francs a year as compensation for his losses.

What are we to make of Mesmer and his Animal Magnetism?
Undoubtedly, he did a lot, albeit unconsciously, to lay some of
the foundations upon which modern psychotherapy rests. He
also was a source of inspiration to countless Quacks from that day
to this. There is little doubt that eventually he became a victim
of his own illusions. The story of the magnetised canary that
used to fly out of a cage in Mesmer's room, perch on his head,
and sing him awake every morning, takes a bit of swallowing.

Even more so, when the clever bird was said to peck a given number of lumps of sugar into Mesmer's coffee cup, at his will.

It is alleged that when Mesmer died, he had a smile on his face. It would be nice to think he was remembering the splendid time he must have had by the Baquet at the Hotel Bullion. Or perhaps, and this is more conjectural, he had at last some perception of just where his extraordinary ideas were going to lead those who came after him.

4.   *More under the Influence*

A few years ago cleaners at the New Horticultural Hall in Westminster witnessed a curious sight. The Annual London Medical Exhibition was in full swing and most of the pharmaceutical firms in Great Britain had taken stands to advertise their products. What intrigued the army of cleaners was this. Before the Exhibition opened a crowd of Drug House representatives seemed always to congregate around one particular stand. There they drank, out of small paper cups, copious drafts of medicine. We must excuse observers coming to the conclusion that this must be really good stuff. What is perhaps more remarkable, this popular medicine was available under the National Health Service.

The secret of the wonderful tonic, so potent that it braced up many stand salesman for the rigours of the day, had nothing to do with the many vitamins it contained. Its amazing popularity came from its sixteen per cent alcohol content.

Alcoholic 'medicines' enjoyed a tremendous vogue in America at the beginning of the 20th century. As we have seen, not a little of Mrs Pinkham's success was due to that ingredient in her Compound. Perhaps the best remembered of the 'whisky tonics' was Peruna. Originally it contained twenty per cent alcohol and very little else. Extensively advertised, it sold by the train-load all over America. It was so popular that eventually various Government Departments found it necessary to impose sanctions. The Office of Indian Affairs notified all their agents that the sale of Peruna was forbidden to Indian territories. 'As a medicine,' they said, 'something else can be substituted, as an intoxicant it has been found too tempting.' Manufacturers were told that unless they modified their formula so that it could no longer be used as a beverage, Peruna would have to be sold under a liquor licence.

'Doc' Hartman, Peruna's inventor, and his advertising partner, Mr Schumacher, got into a huddle and decided to reduce the strength of Peruna to eighteen per cent alcohol, and add certain herbs. This fobbed off meddlesome Government departments until 1920, when further pressure on 'Doc' Hartman persuaded him to give the tonic a 'slight laxative action,' by including a small dose of senna into his formula. This produced what Stewart H. Holbrook called in the *Golden Age of Quackery*, the 'Great Borborigmus Era.' Although the dose of senna contained in a few spoonfuls of Peruna went unnoticed, addicts who regularly drank the product by the bottleful found the laxative a great disadvantage. Peruna sales slumped alarmingly and although the senna was soon removed and replaced by potassium iodide, the number one 'whisky' tonic of America was doomed.

But by now a lot of good had come out of Peruna – for its manufacturers, of course. Doc Hartman was a millionaire many times over, and his fellow director Schumacher when he died recently, left $50,000,000 to the Columbus Gallery of Fine Arts.

Second only to Peruna in its popularity was 'Hostetters Celebrated Stomach Bitters.' These contained twenty-five per cent alcohol, and were actually sold over the counter in the saloons of Alaska, which at this time was a 'dry' State. Pioneers rapidly realised the value of the bitters. The daily dose was equivalent to $1\frac{1}{2}$ ounces of straight whisky. Encouraged by early successes, Hostetters eventually took the strength of their Bitters up to thirty-seven per cent, explaining that this quantity of alcohol was necessary to hold in solution its remarkable ingredients.

But one February night in 1917 brought the celebrated Bitters into disrepute. The Baltimore Sun reported that a large number of drunks had been arrested after over indulgence in a 'certain proprietary medicine.' Hostetters had caused the trouble. After this many teetotallers viewed the famous Bitters with grave suspicion.

G

A similar tonic was Lyko. The advertising of this product was particularly impressive. Lyko not only made you 'feel' ten years younger, but it improved your looks as well. 'Doesn't it make you feel good, cause you to straighten up and feel chesty, when someone guesses your age at ten years younger than you are,' Lyko men asked as they danced around the ballroom with the prettiest girl available? If you did not happen to admire this particular facility, then Lyko was a wonderful sleeping draft, restorative and general tonic. 'It opens up wonderful visions of the future to the downcast, weary and laden souls, depressed in spirit and body,' the manufacturers claimed. This we can well believe when five ounces of Lyko was equivalent to $2\frac{1}{4}$ ounces of gin.

Excellent as these various tonics were for thirsty men and women the world over, they were only copies of a British original some hundred years previously. We do not know the alcoholic strength of Samuel Solomon's Balm of Gilead, but we have a fair indication if we judge by its success. Solomon did not take all the credit for producing the wonderful Balm himself. He rhapsodised that 'its composition has been sanctioned by the most learned physicians of the age, it has preserved its reputation from the period prior to the Birth of Christ, growing in Gilead in Judea in 1730 B.C.' Solomon claimed that he brought the Balm to England by means of a 'secret correspondence with the Honourable East India Company.'

Possibly prejudiced, Solomon was confident as to what might be expected from quaffing the Balm. 'Among Eastern Nations,' he reminisced, 'it has long been a favourite and popular remedy taken internally in cases of diseases of the intestines, ulcers of the lungs, liver and kidneys. Egyptian women possess the wonderful art of rendering themselves fruitful, either by the internal use of the Balm, or by perfuming their bodies with it. The beauty of the skin is said to be not a little improved by it, and ladies of the Seraglio annoint their bodies with it after tepid bathing.'

He went on to say that Frederick the Great cured his famous General Forquet with the Balm of Gilead and added that there was 'incontravenable evidence' that it stayed the ravages of Yellow Fever during the American epidemic of 1800. In more conventional style, Solomon also 'puffed' his Nostrum for 'weak and shattered constitutions, hypochondria, horrors of the mind, sexual debility, intemperance, debauchery, inattention to the necessary cares of health, luxury or studious life.'

Good things can seldom be had for nothing. A small bottle of the cordial Balm of Gilead cost 11/–. The family size containing four times as much cost 33/–. For those whose disorders had 'been for many years in proceeding to such a degree of malignancy as cannot be eradicated in a few weeks,' Solomon advised a crate of three family bottles at the knock-down price of £5.

Such was the demand that he who had started life as a door to door salesman of 'Black Ball' bootpolish, soon had to open up agencies for the handling of his product. There were eventually four hundred odd agencies in England, sixteen in America, and the 'House of Solomon' was represented as far afield as Bengal, Nassau and Quebec. But even with this new found wealth Solomon did not become proud. He could still be consulted for the 'usual compliment of a pound note,' and would give personal advice by letter for a mere 10/6. He was, it hardly seems necessary to add, a graduate of the Marischall College of Aberdeen.

Wealth made Solomon respectable. He bought a nice house built in the Georgian style just outside Liverpool. A picture of the grounds shows two gardeners assiduously working beside an ornamental pond. In these surroundings the élite of the local society were entertained. After one dinner party at which everyone had been wined and dined extremely well, a wag asked Dr Solomon if it would be possible to round off the meal with a few bottles of the Balm of Gilead. The Quack agreed and the Nostrum, which made a good liqueur it is said, was produced. Afterwards, those who had partaken of the remedy were presented with accounts. Solomon explained that he could not mix business with conviviality.

As might be expected the doctor had his critics. A tradesman in Everton found that his wife had changed from being 'modest and temperate,' into a 'dram drinker.' She confessed, under stern interrogation, that her tipple was the Balm of Gilead. Several of her women friends made similar admissions and the husbands in question decided to stop the rot spreading. Calling Solomon out one night on a fool's errand, they waylaid him and after handling him roughly, finally tossed him in a blanket. This was thought a huge joke at the time and an engraving was published showing the incident.

Another harsh critic made his point by giving a public demonstration of 'the effects that the Balm of Gilead had on a pig.' The animal 'yelled most hideously while the medicine was poured down its throat, and afterwards ran about as if mad, endeavouring to bite everything within its reach – in a few minutes it lay down and continued to grunt most piteously until it fell fast asleep.'

Without doubt, Solomon's mixture was very popular in its day. A lot of 'doctors' ' medicine was fairly horrid at this time. Solomon quoted Montaigne as saying, 'whoever saw one physician approve of the prescription of another, without taking something away or adding something to it.' This was probably quite true but it is very doubtful whether the Balm of Gilead contained a trace of its alleged most attractive ingredient – actual gold. Or that it contained a 'secret that physicians failed most egregiously to discover.' In all probability it was pure brandy.

5.   *The Appalling story of the Purge*

Many Quack medicines had strange beginnings. None more so than those of James Morison, the Hygeist, for his 'Vegetable Universal Medicines' were compounded by the admixture of Chronic Hysteria and Masochism.

Little is known of Morison's early days except that he was born in 1770 and that his parents were of great 'affluence and respectability' in Aberdeen. Young James had a University education in Scotland and Germany. Later he lived abroad, first in the chilly Gulf of Riga, but subsequently in the warmer climes of the West Indies and Bordeaux.

It did not seem to matter very much where Morison lived. He suffered just the same. His symptoms leave no doubt in the mind that he was a chronic hysteric. 'Thirty-five years of in-expressible suffering,' he lamented, 'is an event which falls to the lot of few, if any at all.' A selection of his troublesome symptoms included, 'total want of sleep, constant beating and

uneasiness about the heart, dejection, the feeling of something
like a bar about the lower part of my breast, no relish for
amusement, nor anything else, and costiveness.'

The medical profession were singularly at a loss to help the
ailing Aberdonian and he 'ran the gauntlet of all the remedies,
change of air, country amusement, anthelmintics, mercurial and
mineral purges, stomatics and bitters, port wine and beef steak,
cold baths, chalybeats and mineral water, mercury in all its
shapes, salivation, valerian, ether, bark in abundance, laxative
pills and diets.' This was not all. Remedial medicine was called
to the rescue and 'the truss maker was set to work. Steel
jackets were made to spread out the bones of my chest.' All this
was to no avail, and eventually operation was decided upon.
After a weighty consultation between two Physicians and two
Surgeons it was decided to remove Morison's xiphisternum,
the tiny cartilaginous process that lies at the lower end of the
breast bone.

The rationale of such procedure seems obscure to us today,
but the patient's hopes ran high in anticipation of a cure for his
distressing symptomatology. Inevitably surgical intervention
was a failure and poor Morison was left, 'struggling with
disease, the powers of energy of life fast subsiding, the faculties
becoming impaired and the sight becoming dim.'

Exactly what happened next is conjectural. In all probability
Morison's money was getting short and he found that it was
necessary to draw in his horns and live simply. He returned
from his peregrinations abroad to Aberdeen, at the age of
fifty-two, and lived in a house in Silver Street, belonging to a
firm of druggists. Here his hypochondriacal nature was in its
element and he was soon busy studying Pharmacy, and eventually
decided that all his symptoms were due to the 'bad humour,'
that his 'stomach and bowels had diffused over his body.' What
was needed, Morison argued, 'was a Vegetable Universal Compound, to purify the blood and systems.' And so with the aid of
the chemists' Pill machine, he invented his famous remedy. This
was vegetable simplicity in itself, for it consisted solely of a
mixture of aloes and oatmeal.

Having invented this medicine he took it himself. Soon
Morison found all his symptoms had evaporated. Violent
purging with a drug like aloes is not a pleasant experience. It

proved nasty enough to convince Morison that it was doing him a lot of good. What is more he soon had visual evidence of the efficacity of his medicines. He passed a 'substance of a skinny, glutinous nature – four or five inches long, moulded like the gut, which descended from the mouth of the stomach, immediately below the place where the learned doctors and surgeons had begun their incision.' This nasty looking object was used as an advertisement for the Vegetable Universal medicines for many years.

James Morison soon realised that these good things were too precious to be confined to the comparatively sparsely populated North East of Scotland, and he was soon on the way to London, with two casks of pills to conquer the Metropolis.

This he did effectively. Styling himself a Hygeist, his watchword was, 'the old medical science is completely wrong. Hippocrates says Yes, Galen, No. A science without principles is no science at all.' His motto might have been, Purge, Purge and more Purge, for the principles of Hygeism were that if two or three pills did not cure you, taken every day, of course, then try five or six. 'It is impossible,' Morison said, 'that there can be any real cure but by sound purging.'

The offices that he built in Hamilton Place, King's Cross, were soon styled the 'British College of Health.' From here Morison issued bogus medico-scientific papers, such as 'A treatise on the origin of Life,' and 'Some Important advice to the World.' These attempted to explain the theory of his practice. He believed that his invention would cure everything. 'By an effectual and continual purge,' he wrote, 'you will draw down a humour from the eye or remove a corn from the toe. Costiveness may be said to be the mother of all disease.' Even such dire diseases as 'siphylis' (spelling was not Morison's strong point), could be cured by the pills. They were even a preventive for 'all persons acquainted with, and practising the use of the Vegetable Universal Compound, will not have to dread the contagion of this disease. They will prevent and cure it, if already caught.'

Apart from vigorous purgation there was one other method of treatment that Morison approved. The use of the 'flesh brush' was a form of 'sport' much in vogue in the early 19th century. 'This was,' the Hygeist explained, 'the only external application the body requires, as the Vegetable Universal Medicine is the only internal one.' He based his advice on the experience of an old, retired Naval officer, Admiral Henry, of Rolvenden in Kent. The Admiral had become 'very infirm from rheumatism and other disorders, and accordingly he began beating and hammering all the parts affected with hard instruments made for the purpose.' Strangely enough this soon produced a cure.

Morison was persuaded that the flesh brush, 'passed with a strong hand over every part of the body, for a good while twice a day, prepares it for exercise and prevents fatigue.' The instruments necessary for this treatment were 'all of a violent description, made of bits of wood, but finding these excoriated the skin, bone was tried and answered the object in view.'

It is obvious that Morison believed this modified flagellation a great advantage. As a practice it was very common in England in the 18th and 19th centuries. The period has even been referred to as the Era of Flagellomania. Many sumptuous houses were established in London to cater for this extraordinary cult. Certain ladies were known as celebrated 'whippers.' Mrs Collett was one of these and George IV is reported to have visited her house in Tavistock Court. Perhaps the most famous of these 'governesses,' as they were sometimes called, was Mrs Teresa Berkeley, who lived at 28, Charlotte Street, Portland Place. She invented the 'Berkeley Horse,' a curious padded trestle upon which 'anyone with plenty of money could be birched, whipped, fustigated, scourged, needle-pricked, holly-brushed, furze-brushed, or phlebotomised, until he had had a bellyful.'

It is an interesting facet in Morison's character that he combined the internal scourging of the body by means of his pills with external scourging by means of flagellation. Most of the flagellants were of course men and women who had become tired of the more conventional methods of debauchery, and to whom either being whipped themselves, or watching others, provided a new experience to excite their jaded passions.

Once Morison's reputation was established, he flourished. He published his eight principles of Hygeian theory that boil down to the fact that, once again, by purgation all diseases can be cured. Titled patients wrote eulogical testimonials on how Mr Morison's Vegetable Universal Medicines cured them, their husbands and their maids. A petition was even made to Parliament asking for a Select Committee to consider the Hygeian system in the interests of Medical Science.

After his years of 'suffering,' the years of success must have rolled by quickly for Morison. With all his curious neurotic and masochistic traits he appears to have been sincere in his beliefs, for it was reported that when he died at the age of seventy he was reaching for another dose of the Universal Medicine.

His competence as a Quack may be assessed by the fact that he left a fortune of £500,000 and was buried in a 'family tomb in Kensal Green Cemetery, nearly as large as a park lodge,' irrevocable evidence, surely, of the power of the purge.

❧ 11 ❧

FINALE

The 20th century brought many changes to Quackery. Some species have entirely disappeared. The wandering Mountebank has become almost extinct. One of the last of this type was Dr Bossy. He was a regular 'performer' in Covent Garden, every Thursday afternoon for many years.

His stage platform, raised some six feet from the ground, was reached by means of a step-ladder. In the centre an armchair was provided for the patient. Dr Bossy stood slightly behind and next to a table that displayed impressive surgical instruments. Elsewhere on the platform was a medicine chest containing the Quack's stock in trade.

Bossy was always impeccably dressed and wore a gold-laced cocked hat. He bowed respectfully to the audience before giving his address. A verbatim account of one of these is preserved in F. B. Winslow's *Memoirs* from which this is taken:

An aged woman was helped up the ladder, and seated in the chair; she had been deaf, nearly blind, and was also lame; indeed, she might have been said to have been visited with Mrs Thrale's three warnings, and death would have walked in at her door, only Dr Bossy blocked up the passage.

The doctor asked questions with an audible voice, and the patient responded – he usually repeating the response, in his Anglo-German dialect.

DOCTOR: Dis poora voman vot is – how old vosh you?

OLD WOMAN: I be almost eighty, sir; seventy-nine last lady-day, old style.

DOCTOR: Ah, tat is an incurable disease.

PATIENT: O dear, O dear! Say not so-incurable! Why, you have restored my sight – I can hear again and I can walk without my crutches.

DOCTOR (smiling): No, no, good womans, old age is vot incurable; but, by the blessing of Gote, I will cure you of vot is ilshe. Dis poora voman vos lame and deaf, and almost blind. How many hosipetals have you been in?

PATIENT: Three, sir; St Thomas's, St Bartholomew's, and St George's.

DOCTOR: Vot, and you found no reliefs? Vot, none – not at alls?

PATIENT: No, none at all, sir.

DOCTOR: And how many professioners have attended you?

PATIENT: Some twenty or thirty, sir.

DOCTOR: O mine Gote! Three sick hosipetals, and dirty (thirty) doctors! I should vonder vot you have not enough to kill you twenty times. Dis poora vomans has become mine patient. Doctor Bossy gain all patients bronounced ingurables; pote wid de plessing of Brovidence, I shall make short work of it, and set you upon your legs again. Goode peoples, dis poora vomans vos teaf as a toor nails (holding up his watch to her ear, and striking the repeater). Can you hear dat pell?

PATIENT: Yes, sir.

DOCTOR: O den be thankful to Gote. Can you valk round this chair (offering his arm)?

PATIENT: Yes, sir.

DOCTOR: Sit down, again, good vomans. Can you see?

PATIENT: Pretty so so, doctor.

DOCTOR: Vot can you see, good vomans?

PATIENT: I can see the baker there (pointing to a mutton-pie man, with his board on his head).

DOCTOR: And vot else can you, good vomans?

OLD WOMAN: The poll-parrot there (pointing to Richardson's Hotel). 'Lying old —' screamed Richardson's poll-parrot. All the crowd shouted with laughter. Dr Bossy waited until the laugh had subsided, and looking across the way, significantly shook his head at the parrot, and gravely exclaimed, laying his hand on his bosom, ' 'Tis no lie, you silly pird, 'tis all true as is de gospel.'

Perhaps Quacks of Bossy's type are not sophisticated enough for modern tastes. The general public enjoys a higher level of education now than it did at the turn of the century. Luckily for the Quacks, we have not become less credulous with more sophisticated learning. When Voltaire wrote that Quackery was born when the first knave met the first fool he was not entirely right. It is not necessary to be foolish to be credulous.

There is one big difference between trying to appraise a Cure and the inherent value of tangible things. Education and experience give us a good idea of the quality of a book, car or a pair of shoes, but the effect of somebody's cure for a cold, rheumatism or a headache is more difficult to assess. There is a twofold reason for this. First of all there is a natural tendency to recover spontaneously from most diseases. If this was not so the human race would soon be extinct. Secondly, the large proportion of the symptoms that make people believe they are ill are quite unrelated to any physical disease at all. Psychosomatic symptoms are, as we have seen, very susceptible to suggestion as a cure. These two factors working together make it highly probable that Quackery will be always with us.

The way Quacks have changed with the times is interesting. An insignificant but astute nostrum hawker who once owned a tiny shop in St Helens, Lancashire, started a business that eventually became one of the largest Pharmaceutical Houses in this country. Joseph Beecham was advertising his pills in newspapers and magazines at the end of the last century in the best traditions of Quackery. They 'worked like magic,' he told the eager readers of the *Young Ladies' Journal*, and 'will be found to work wonders on the most important organs in the human machine.' 'For females of all ages,' the pills were especially recommended as they carried off 'all humours in a few days.' Beecham took one of the original prizes for therapeutic benevolence. His pills, 'pearls of great value, more precious than gold or silver,' were worth, it will be remembered, a 'guinea a box.' They sold for a mere ninepence.

That indefatigable Quack harrier, the Editor of *Health News*, tried to unravel the mystery of this startling act of charity and drew up the following account sheet:

(1) Value of box of pills according to Beecham – £1 1s. 0d.
(2) Amount received – 9d.
(3) Actual loss per box – £1 0s. 3d.

This 'inexplicable' result led the Editor to submit a packet of Beecham's pills to a public analyst. He reported that 'the pills consist solely of aloes and ginger mixed up with soap.' The estimated cost of a box of pills was less than half a farthing. The humour here is rather obtuse and the exposé probably did little harm to Beecham. His descendants realised before any

other patent medicine manufacturer in England, the power of
advertising. Sir Joseph Beecham was proud to tell the Select
Committee on Patent Medicines in 1913 that his business was
making one million pills per day.

Eventually the Beecham group of Companies decided to
reform and developed an ethical products business. During
recent years they have established vast research laboratories
from which have emerged the first of the new synthetic
penicillins.

• Perhaps the most important date as far as English Quackery
is concerned was 1858. This is when the Medical Registration
Act became law and the General Medical Council came into
being. Until this Act was passed only about a third of the doctors
in these Islands thought it necessary to hold a medical qualification of any kind. Afterwards only practitioners on the Register
could sign death certificates and certain minimum standards for
Registration were introduced.

America lagged behind in this matter. Due to pioneer conditions and individual State rights, American 'doctors' were a
much more varied breed than their British counterparts. During
the 19th century, over 400 medical schools were formed in
America, few of which had any connection with hospitals or
universities. Many of them were very irregularly run and some
of the lecturers were not even medical men themselves. Nevertheless, two years' study qualified a man to practise.

Even in Universities like Harvard, the curriculum consisted
of a four-month course of lectures repeated every year. Many
medical students were said hardly to have been able to write,
let alone take examinations. It was not until 1905 that the
American Medical Association pressed effectively for reforms,
and 1910 before an informative report by Abraham Flexner
finally introduced more or less universal standards in the various
States of America.

Once the two nations had a workable formula that could be
applied to differentiate the real doctor from the Quack, big
changes took place. But it was years before the old Diploma
Mills, where 'doctors' ' Diplomas were produced for a consideration, finally closed down.

One of the most interesting and last of these was the 'St Luke's
Hospital of Niles, Michigan.' It is doubtful if there was one

patient ever admitted into this 'hospital,' although it advertised itself as being 'situated in the beautiful and healthy centre of the Great Fruit Belt of Michigan, and supplied with all the latest surgical instruments for performing the important as well as minor operations.' Nearer the truth was the claim that 'expert operators,' were always ready to 'assist at operations,' and that, 'terms were made to suit the physician in every case.' Anyone aspiring to a medical degree at the hospital merely filled in a form headed, 'Physicians' Application to be placed on the staff of St Luke's Hospital, Niles, Michigan.'

Once 'accepted' as a member of the staff of the non-existent hospital, run by two Quacks of the old school, Dr C. W. H. B. Granville and Dr Arthur C. Probert, a handsome Diploma was rapidly issued. It was artistically lithographed (17 in. × 22 in.) and entirely written in Latin apart from one prominent line that declared the candidate to be a 'Doctor of Medicine and Surgery.' At the bottom left-hand corner of the Diploma was a 'large, Corporate Gold Seal,' from which emerged two handsome pieces of blue ribbon.

These certificates, it was alleged, were 'a great attraction to any physician's office, and imparted a confidence to visitors and patients.' Candidly enough the medical directors of St Luke's said that their product had the appearance of 'regular Hospital Medical Diplomas.' The prices seem reasonable even in the 1900's. If finished on heavy royal linen they cost five dollars each. On imitation parchment the price went up to seven dollars, fifty, and a young physician who felt that money was of a secondary consideration could have his diploma set out on genuine sheepskin for a mere ten dollars.

Any Doctor today who appears in Court is asked, directly after he has sworn the oath and identified himself, if he is a Registered Medical Practitioner. The importance of Registration as a differentiation between qualified doctor and Quack is therefore underlined in Courts of Law almost daily. Fringe practitioners and Quacks must always answer this pertinent question in the negative.

The wily mind of the Quack has thus been forced to jettison the whole idea of posing as a doctor. Undismayed, he has invented specialities of his own that are often very difficult to define and almost impossible to legislate against. The dawn of the Medical Register was also a great stimulus to the Fringe Practitioner.

One of the earliest developments in Fringe practice was Osteopathy. It is curious that a 'science' should have been invented or discovered by any one person, but this was the case in 1874 when Andrew Taylor Still 'flung to the breeze the banner of Osteopathy.' Still was a curious man, even more curious is the story of the evolution of his new 'science.' As far as medicine was concerned Still had only a fragmentary education. (He attended the Kansas City School of Physicians and Surgeons but left before he had completed his course to enlist and fight in the Civil War.)

His father had been a jack of all trades and one trade that he had far from mastered was medicine. Despite this handicap he is thought to have imparted something of a medical background to young Andrew. In Still's autobiography there is a picture of a young Cavalry officer in battle, who we must presume is the inventor himself, as it is labelled 'osteopathy in danger.'

One day when the fighting had died down Still became interested in some bones that had been dug up from an old Indian graveyard. Such was his power of perception, we are told, that he could soon name each of these, even when blindfold, and could actually state from which side of the body they came! Impressed with the miraculous power that he possessed Still went on to elaborate a theory of disease with reference to his discoveries. He called the new science Osteopathy (literally, bone-suffering). Conventional medicine had been quite wrong up to date, Still claimed. All illness was due to malpositions or subluxations of the joints in the spine. By manipulation of the spine every disease could be cured.

'Lung fever,' the pedagogue said, was caused by disturbances of the vertebrae high up in the neck. Typhoid, dysentery, appendicitis, cancer, and the whole host of 'female complaints' were due to trouble in the lower vertebrae. At a later date Still changed his mind on some of these diseases and wrote to the *Ladies' Home Journal* to this effect: 'I do not believe that there are such diseases as Fever, Typhoid, Typhus, Rheumatism, Sciatica, Gout, Colic, Liver diseases or Croup,' he proudly announced. When patients suffer, he said, 'it is because their nerves and vessels are interfered within their spinal columns and on the way up.'

Later in his career Still was convinced he had been given his amazing power of healing by the Almighty himself, and that he was a sort of orthopaedic ministering angel. To quote his own words, 'shame on the knife that cuts a woman like a Christmas hog. Almost one-half the women of today bear a knife-mark, and I tell you, God's intelligence is reproached by it. An Osteopath stands firm in the belief that God knew what to arm the world with, and follows His principles. And he who so far forgets God's teachings as to use drugs, forfeits the respect of this school and its teachings. God is the Father of Osteopathy, and I am not ashamed of the child of His mind.'

Modern Osteopathy would like to forget its curious founder. To a large extent it has grown away from mystical ideas and its practitioners obtain all the diagnostic aid that they can from X-rays and blood counts. In England a Register of Osteopaths and two Approved Training Schools teach the present-day principles of Osteopathy. One of these schools caters exclusively for medical practitioners who wish to specialise in this subject.

There is evidence that the Medical Profession and the Osteopaths may be trying to get together. The *B.M.J.* recently reminded its readers of Sir James Paget telling his colleagues at Bart's, some eighty years ago, 'that if they did not learn how to manipulate their patients they would lose them to the bonesetters.' The *Journal* continued, 'Many years later the bone-setter Sir Herbert Barker showed by the great success of his life and work that the medical profession had still not learnt Sir James Paget's lesson. A profession which struck the unfortunate Dr Axham off the Register for giving anaesthetics to Barker's patients ended up by almost canonising Barker at a meeting held in his honour by the British Orthopaedic Association in 1936.' If the courtship between the two professions is cool at the moment, it is the Osteopaths rather than the doctors who will not be wooed. Perhaps they fear that the niggardly fees allowed by the State to the medical profession in general are not sufficiently impressive to tempt them to lose their independent status.

Chiropractice might be described as Osteopathy's skeleton in the cupboard. In America, where it must be admitted that even

Osteopaths are still very heavily criticised by the medical profession, Chiropractice is always the territory of the Quack and medical 'Con' man. The science's founder, Daniel D. Palmer, was a fishmonger before he saw the light. But it was his son who really developed Chiropractice in America into the big business it is today. Its devotees seem to stick to the wilder premises of early Osteopaths. For example, they still teach that bacterial diseases, such as diphtheria and scarlet fever, are best cured by manipulating the spine, echoing the original ideas of the old Master.

The bogus nature of American chiropractice is demonstrated in one of Palmer's inventions in the 1920's. He called it the neurocalometer. This consisted of two simple thermopiles which were placed on either side of a patient's spine. Wires ran from these to sensitive galvanometers from which were obtained the neurocalometer 'readings.' This invention was leased by Palmer to chiropractors for $2,200, $1,000 down and $10 per month for ten years. The lessees of these extraordinary machines had to promise not to tamper with them in any way and to charge patients a flat rate of at least ten dollars for a neurocalometer reading. As an encore Palmer invented another diagnostic machine with which he obviously hoped to relieve sufferers from the dire effects of particularly troublesome subluxations. He called it the Electroencephaloneuromentimpograph. Just what this did is anybody's guess.

Another popular form of Fringe practice is Naturopathy. Unlike Osteopathy it had no official founder but that does not mean it has lacked success. Geoffrey Murray wrote in the *Spectator*, October 1960, that it was impossible to provide a working definition of Naturopathy. 'In its best known form,' he said, 'it consists of elegant and expensive fasting – the physical equivalent of the spiritual retreat, a penance which some men and women are willing to suffer gladly once a year.'

In America the 'science' is more highly developed and there are many branches of this interesting and relatively harmless form of Quackery. One, which must surely take a prize for idiocy, is Iridiagnosis. Practitioners of this art merely gaze into their patient's eyes and see, in one of forty or more different zones in the iris, the marks of disease. These stigmata are then related to areas in the body and a diagnosis is 'clinched.' One of the leading exponents of Iridiagnosis thought it necessary to give his pupils a few tips on recognising glass eyes in patients as these could make for embarrassing errors in diagnosis.

Modern Naturopathy has to some extent moved from such fascinating theory and joins hands firmly with Mother Nature endorsing Health Foods, Fruit Juices, strange milk food products, and Chlorophyll. It has an absolute antipathy to regular Medicine. Some of the more recent facets of Naturopathic practice have included weird ideas about fertilisers and insecticides. In several shops in London today you can pay well over the market price for poor, deformed carrots and scabby apples that have been grown in the 'natural' way.

It is unlikely that anybody reading this book will have a career in Quackery in mind, either for themselves or their children. And yet should anyone want to make a lot of money quickly there are few 'professions' that offer such opportunities. Of course, it is necessary to steer clear of anything illegal and keep a wary eye on the rules and regulations relevant to medicines and foodstuffs. But there is one thing that should never worry a prospective Quack. It is not at all necessary to have a 'cure' that 'works.' Some of the most successful Quack practice has been in fields where the therapeutic future might be deemed as being distinctly gloomy.

Cures for baldness are an example of this. The almost universal prevalence of some degree of this disability in men over the age of 35 shows that loss of hair on the male head is practically a *sine qua non* of maturity.

A very small proportion of all baldness is due to physical or psychological disease. But well over 90 per cent is of the common or patterned type, unassociated with any local or systemic pathology. It is unfortunately completely resistant to treatment and is a hereditary condition that can be transmitted via women to their sons. As it is associated with the development of secondary sexual characteristics the only possible cure, or prevention rather, is castration. Eunuchs who are 'treated' in this way before puberty never go bald.

It might be thought, therefore, that Hair Growing Quackery would be fraught with difficulties and failure for its exploiters. The facts prove otherwise. For many years now hundreds of baldness cures have prospered in a really remarkable way.

Anyone who picked up a newspaper or magazine at the turn of the century would be confronted with excessively shaggy ladies and gentlemen advertising such hirsute boons as Edwards' Harlene. Mr L. S. Edwards assured us that his product would grow 'luxurious hair, whiskers, moustachios, heavily in a few weeks without injury to the skin and no matter what age. As a producer of whiskers and moustachios it has never been equalled. As a curer of weak or thin eyelashes or restoring grey hair to its original colour, it never fails.' Harlene, readers were told, was pronounced by physicians and analysts to be perfectly harmless and devoid of any metallic or other injurious ingredients. Hair tonics have never been cheap, but Mr Edwards advertised in a typical example of Quack generosity, offering, for a limited period only, a 5/6 trial bottle for the ridiculous sum of 3/6.

The treatment of baldness is as popular today with Quacks as it was at the beginning of the century. Of course, prices have increased. One famous London clinic charges over £140, for a six-month course of treatment that may or may not improve the condition of the scalp. The one thing that it certainly does not do is cure common or patterned baldness.

Should any young fringe practitioner feel that the modern hair clinic racket is fully exploited, or that eventually some form of legislation may be devised that will prevent his unwary patients being relieved of some surplus cash, let him take heart. There are still plenty of excellent opportunities available. Dr Albert Abrams started a business over 50 years ago that is going strong today. He began life as a regular physician and obtained a Heidelberg M.D. in 1882. After carrying out various post-graduate studies in Europe, he returned to practise in his native San Francisco. Sometime around 1910 Dr Abrams seems to have decided that there was something unsatisfying about Medicine and directed his nimble brain to other fields of endeavour.

His subsequent career will serve as an example to any young man who feels as Albert did, and wants to throw convention to the winds and launch himself into the exciting business of fringe Medicine. The first thing that Dr Abrams did was to invent his own speciality. He called it Spondylotherapy. Having invented it he wrote a book about it. This was an immense success and quickly went through several editions. With such public interest being shown, Dr Abrams, unselfish to a T when it came to dissipating medical knowledge, gave instruction in Spondylo-therapy to would-be disciples at a mere 200 dollars a course.

The principle of the therapy seems obscure to us today. It had something to do with percussion of the spine and Dr Abrams' more professional colleagues callously referred to the new art as a 'hybrid of up-stage osteopathy and chiropractice.' Not dismayed, the inventor formed an Association for the study of his speciality, which eventually became the American Association for Medico-Physical Research, and a Mecca for faddists of all types.

Whether or not Dr Abrams found spine tapping a little hard on the fingers we do not know, but later he forsook this rather rigid structure as a percussion site for the more resonant abdomen. Many people have succeeded by experimenting in something new which catches the public's imagination. In the same way as Graham used electricity, Abrams exploited the new science of Radio. He invented a diagnostic machine that he called the Dynamizer.

The method of working the Dynamizer was rather compli-cated but it had several advantages quackwise. A drop of blood from a sick patient was put on a piece of blotting paper inside the machine. A wire led from the apparatus to the forehead of a healthy person, who stood facing West, stripped to the waist, in a dim light. Dr Abrams then used this person's abdomen as a sort of diagnostic sounding board and by mapping out areas of 'dullness' on his assistant's abdomen, eventually pronounced judgement on the blood sample in the Dynamizer.

This amazing technique caught on. Soon Abrams 'found' that he could do without the blood sample, the signature of the prospective patient worked just as well. To their surprise sub-cribers to Abrams' House Journal, *Physico-Clinical Medicine*, read that the master could not only diagnose disease but religion as well. Dr Abrams told his students that if they would 'conduct energy at V.R.6 and use the S.V. reactions,' it was possible to diagnose at least six religions from abdominal percussion. Some-time during the early 1920's Albert Abrams realised that he was missing out on something. It was all very well diagnosing with the Dynamizer but what about treatment? He doubtless had the thought at the back of his mind that patients might slip back into the hands of the regular physicians for their therapy. Eventually this was put right, for the Ossilloclast was invented.

This apparatus cured, Abrams claimed, by means of vibratory impulses. He explained that drugs, when they influenced diseases, did so because they had the same vibratory rate as the disease in question. But drugs could be dangerous, the doctor argued, and anyway he was not in the drug business. Far more effective, he was persuaded, were radio waves that would vibrate disorders out of the most delicate tissues.

Just how successful the Ossilloclasts were is shown by the money they earned for Abrams. Like the Dynamizers they were never sold outright, but leased to special operators for 250 dollars per year plus a 200-dollar postal training course. The hirers had to agree never to open up one of these magic boxes to see what made it tick. At one time Abrams was taking 1,500 dollars per month from machine rents alone. When he died in 1923 he left over two million dollars.

Long before this sad day medical Philistines were doing their best to discredit Abrams. One doctor sent a piece of blotting paper with some guineapig's blood on it for the Dynamizer to work on. The diagnosis came back that the patient had 'general cancer and tuberculosis of the genito-urinary tract.' Someone else submitted a sample of sheep's blood. This time the diagnosis was hereditary syphilis, and a guaranteed cure was offered for a mere 250 dollars. Later, some sceptical members of the American Medical Association got hold of one of the wonderful machines and took it to pieces. The box contained a mass of Ammeters, Resistances, Condensers and other electrical apparatus, all connected together without any rhyme or reason.

It might be assumed that when Abrams died, Electronic Reactions Abrams, to give the method its official name, would fade out. But this did not occur for here we are not dealing with a personality cult. The fascination of E.R.A. was wireless waves and vibrations. These are as good a draw today as they were in the 1920's. The Electromedical Foundation, originated by Abrams, is still at work in San Francisco, publishing the *Medical Electronic Digest*, and generally carrying on in the old traditions of its founder. The food and drug administration in America estimates that some 5,000 electronic reaction machines were being used by Osteopaths and other Fringe practitioners up and down the country, as recently as 1954. The therapeutic units now leased by the Electromedical Foundation to interested operators are reported to be small shortwave radio transmitters.

A Los Angeles specialist, Dr Ruth B. Drown, uses machines similar to the Abrams models and has a vast practice that includes many celebrities and film stars. When the American Medical Association investigated her in 1950, they dismissed her results as being completely unimpressive. Practically speaking she goes one step further than Abrams and diagnoses her cases by radio.

A High Court case brought by Miss Katherine Phillips against Mr George de la Warr in 1960, shows that the spirit of Albert Abrams is still with us. The de la Warr instrument, manufactured and sold for £110 each, is popularly known as the Black Box. Into this invention go the traditional blood samples on blotting paper. A modification on the original Abrams' model is a rubber 'detector' on the box that has to be stroked with the middle finger while various dials are adjusted. The friction is continued until the finger 'sticks.' The dials are then consulted and a diagnosis is obtained. Miss Phillips sued Mr de la Warr for damages, alleging fraud. Miss Philips lost her case and it was decided that Mr de la Warr believed in his invention and that there was no misrepresentation.

The Defence in the Black Box Case rested on the definition of Radionics. Mr Humphreys, representing de la Warr, was reported as pleading that 'a radionic diagnosis is not claimed to be on a physical plane. Again and again it is stressed it is pre-physical. The case for the Defence will be as it always has been, that the experiments show that certain things happen and continue to happen again and again. We call them pre-physical because it does not seem physical.'

On this reasoning it was cleverly explained that a spot of blood from a new-born baby might be diagnosed radionically as being leukaemic. Of course, it would be impossible to prove that the radionic diagnosis might not be a physical one at some much later date.

Although men of science may have thought the procedure scientifically baseless, the manufacturers of the Black Box persuaded the Court that they believed in their product. Mr de la Warr seemed utterly convinced that, properly handled by the right person, the Black Box did everything that was expected of it and Miss Philips lost her case.

Whether or not anyone believes that there is anything in the science of Radionics is purely a matter of personal opinion. Even leaving it aside there are still plenty of opportunities available in Fringe Medicine. There is still plenty of room at the top for the right man. It is over one hundred years since Robert Southey wrote the following words, but they demonstrate how little change there has been in the Natural History of Quackery, in modern times: 'Man is a dupable animal. Quacks in Medicine, Religion and Politics know this and act on that knowledge. There is scarcely anyone who may not like a trout, be taken by tickling.'

BIBLIOGRAPHY

AMERICAN MED. ASSN., *Nostrums and Quackery*, 1912, 1921, 1936.

ANGELO, HENRY, *Reminiscences*, Colborn & Bentley, 1830.

ANNALS OF ROYAL COLLEGE OF PHYSICIANS.

ARCHENHOLTZ, J. W., *A Picture of England*, 1787.

BESANT, W., *London in the 18th Century*, 1902.

BLACK, W. G., *Folk Medicine*, Folk Lore Soc., 1883.

BRAYLEY, E. WEDLAKE, *History of Surrey*.

BRITISH JOURNAL OF OPHTHALMOLOGY, Pulman, 1930.

BRITISH MEDICAL ASSN., *Secret Remedies*, 1909; *More Secret Remedies*, 1912.

BRODIE, BENJ., *Works Of*, Longman, 1865.

BRODUM, WM., *A Guide to Old Age*, 1795.

BUCHAN, WM., *Domestic Medicine*, Oddy, 1813.

BURTON, JEAN, *Lydia Pinkham is Her Name*, Farrar, Straus & Co., 1949.

CAVALLO, TIBERIUS, *An Essay on the Theory and Practice of Med. Electricity*, 1781.

CHAMBERS, *Book of Days, Vol. 1*.

CHANCELLOR, E. BERESFORD, *Pleasure Haunts of London*, Constable, 1925.

CLUTTON, JO., *A true and candid Relation of the good and bad effects of Josh. Ward's Pill and Drop*.

COATS, G., *London Ophthalmic Hospital Reports*, 1915.

CORRY, J., *Detection of Quackery*, 1802.

COURTENAY, F. B., *Revelations of Quacks and Quackery*, Bailliere, Tyndall, Cox, 1885.

EDITOR OF HEALTH NEWS, *Exposures of Quackery, Vols. I and II*, 1895.

EVERITT, GRA., *Doctors and Doctors*, 1888.

FARRE, F. J., *Short History of Royal College of Physicians*.

FISHBEIN, MORRIS, *Fads and Quackery in Healing*, 1933.

FRAXI PISANUS, *Centuria Librorum Absconditorum*.

GARDNER, M., *Fads and Fallacies*, Dover Pubs., 1952.

GRAHAM, JAMES, *An address to the Inhabitants of Great Britain*, 1775.
A clear, full and faithful Portraiture of a certain most beautiful spotless Virgin Princess, 1779.
Il Corvito Amoroso — delivered to the Temple of Hymen, 1782.

A lecture on the Generation Increase and Improvement of the Human species, 1783.

GIFFORD, ED., *The Evil Eye*, Macmillan, 1958.

GOLDSMITH, MARGARET, *Franz Anton Mesmer*, Barker, 1934.

GOODALL, CHAS., *Historical accounts of the College's proceedings against Empirics and Irregular Practitioners*, 1684.

GOULD AND PYLE, *Anomalies of Medicine*, Saunders, 1901.

GREEN, ROB. E., *Quips from an Upstart Courier*, 1590.

GROSE, FRANCIS, *Grose's Classical Dictionary*, 1823; *A Guide to Health*, 1773.

GUTHRIE, D., *A History of Medicine*, Nelson, 1945.

HANCOCK, D. D., *Febrifugum Magnum*, 1722.

HALFORD, SIR H., *Physic and Physicians, Vol. I*, Longman, 1839.

HALLE, JOHN, *An Historical Expostulation*, R. Richards, 1565.

HARTLEY, DAVID, *A view of the present Evidence for and against Mrs Stephens*, 1739.

HEALING ART, THE, Ward, Downey, 1887.

HOLBROOK, S. H., *Golden Age of Quackery*, Macmillan, 1959.

HOME, G., *Epsom, its History and Surroundings*, Homeland Assn, 1901.

HURD MEAD, K. A., *History of Women in Medicine*, Haddam Press, 1938.

JAMES, R., *A Medical Dictionary*, 1745.

JEAFFRESON, J. CORDY, *A Book about Doctors*, New York, 1851.

JOHNSON, ED., *Johnson's Practice of Hydropathy*, Simpkin & Marshall, 1858.

JONES, WM., *Credulities Past and Present*, Chatto & Windus, 1880.

JOURNALS OF HOUSE OF COMMONS, 1716.

KAY, JOHN, *Edinburgh Portraits*, 1885.

KING, LESTER P., *Medical World of the 18th century*, Chicago Press, 1958.

LAWRENCE, ROB., *Primitive Psychotherapy and Quackery*, Houghton, 1910.

LONG, JOHN ST JOHN, *Discoveries in the Science and Art of Healing*, 1831. *A critical Exposure of the Ignorance and malpractice of certain Medical Practitioners*, 1831.

LYSONS, DANIEL, *Collectianea*, 1661–1840.

MALCOLM, JAMES PELLER, *London – Anecdotes during 18th century*, Longman, 1810.

MEDICAL ESSAY AND OBSERVATIONS, Edinburgh, 1771.

MEDICINA FLAGELLATA OR THE DOCTOR SCARIFIED, London, 1721.

MERRYWEATHER, F., *Glimmerings in the Dark*, Simpkin, 1850.

MESMER, *Mesmerism*, 1779.

MINTY MARCHANT, *Medical Quackery*, Heinemann, 1932.

MODERN QUACK OR MEDICAL IMPOSTOR, 1724.

MOORE ISABELLA, *The Useful and Entertaining Family Miscellany*, 1772.

MORAN LORD, *The Harveian Oration on Credulity*, Lancet, 1954.

MORISON JAMES, *Morisoniana or The Family Adviser*, London College of Health, 1839.

NOCTURNAL REVELS OR HISTORY OF KING'S PLACE, 1779.

PETTIGREW, T. J., *Medical Portrait Gallery*, 1838–40.

POWNALL, HENRY, *History of Epsom*, Dorling, 1825.

PRACTITIONER 78, *Some Famous Quacks – Sir Wm. Read*, 1907.
Some Famous Quacks – Joshua Ward, 1907.

PROFESSIONAL ANECDOTES, V. II, 1825.

QUACKS AND QUACKERY BY A MEDICAL PRACTITIONER, 1844.

READ, SIR W., *A short and exact account of all Disease incident to the Eye*.

ROLLESTON, SIR HUMPHREY, *Irregular Practice and Quackery*, 1927.

SANGER, W. W., *History of Prostitution*, 1919.

SARTORIUS, SINEGRADIBUS, *A faithful and full account of the surprising life and adventures of the Celebrated Sartorius Sinegradibus (Edinburgh)*, 1740.

SMITH, J. T., *Nollekens and his Times*.

SOLOMON, SAM., M.D., *A Guide to Health*.

SPRIGGE, S. S., *Life and Times of Thos. Wakley*, 1897.

STUBBS, S. G. BLAXLAND, *Sixty Centuries of Health and Physic*, Sampson Low, 1931.

SYDNEY, W. C., *England and the English in the 18th century*, 1891.

TAYLOR, JOHN OPHTHALMIATER, *History of the Travels and Adventures of the Chevalier, John Taylor*, 1761.

TAYLOR, JOHN (HENRY JONES) *Life and Extraordinary History of Chevalier John Taylor*, 1761.

TIMBS, J., *Doctors and Patients*, Bentley, 1873.

THOMPSON, C. J., *Quacks of Old London*, Bretanos, 1928.
Magic and Healing, Rider & Co.

TURNER, E. S., *Call the Doctor*, Michael Joseph, 1958.
Shocking History of Advertising, Michael Joseph, 1952.

TYLOR, ED. B., *Primitive Culture*, Murray, 1920.

WADD, WM., *Nugae Chirurgicae*, 1824.

WALSH, JAMES J., *Cures – or Cures that Fail*, Appleton, New York, 1923.

WALPOLE, H., *Letters (ed. Cunningham)*.

WESLEY, JOHN, *Primitive Physic*, 1807.

INDEX

219